FUTURE FLIGHT

The Next Generation of
Aircraft Technology

FUTURE FLIGHT

The Next Generation of
Aircraft Technology

Bill Siuru and John D. Busick

TAB BOOKS
Blue Ridge Summit, PA

FIRST EDITION
FIFTH PRINTING

© 1989 by **TAB Books**.
TAB Books is a division of McGraw-Hill, Inc.

Library of Congress Cataloging-in-Publication Data

Siuru, Bill, 1938 –
    Future flight : the next generation of aircraft technology / by
  Bill Siuru and John D. Busick.
      p.   cm.
    Includes index.
    ISBN 0-8306-7415-2   ISBN 0-8306-9415-3 (pbk.)
    1. Airplanes—Technological innovations.   I. Busick, John D.
  II. Title.
  TL671.S565   1987
  629.133′34—dc19
                                          87-26233
                                          CIP

Front Cover Inset: An artist's concept of the National Aerospace Plane.
(Courtesy Rockwell International)

Front Cover: A version of the Advanced Tactical Fighter. (Courtesy Lockheed-
California)

This book is dedicated to the hope that the machines of Future Flight will be used for the benefit of mankind and not its destruction.

*Light from the past shines on the present
and lights the pathway into the future.*

John Busick, 1987

Contents

Preface

SINCE THE BEGINNING of history, man has yearned to reach for the heavens. Long before flight was thought possible, the wings of eagles, appearing on the art of ancient Egypt, the staffs of Roman legions, and the Great Seal of the United States, represented man's thirst for flight. American Indians revered the eagle because it represented the lofty ideal of their spirits leaving the bonds of earth and soaring to the heavens.

When flight became possible, the eagle symbology was still there. Charles Lindbergh was known as the "Lone Eagle." And who will ever forget the transmission from the moon, "the Eagle has landed"? Today, one of the U.S. Air Force's finest air superiority fighters is the F-15 *Eagle*. The aircraft of the future will combine the spirit of the eagle with the ingenuity of man.

The past three decades have seen military and commercial aircraft routinely fly at more than twice the speed of sound. Travel by air has progressed from a means of transportation for the privileged, and for special occasions, to the most popular means of traveling distances greater than a few hundred miles. And travel into space, while not yet routine, is a familiar event.

As an engineer advancing technology and as a military pilot using these advances in technology, we have not only watched the rapid progress of aviation, we have had an active part in it. This intimate experience with what has happened in the past, along with the knowledge of what is going on now in the aerospace world, allows us to project what will be happening in the future.

Introduction

THE DEVELOPMENT of most aviation concepts usually follows a rather orderly process from the gleam in the eyes of the engineer and scientist to the final aircraft in the hands of the military, commercial, or private pilot. Whether the aircraft is a fast fighter or a luxurious executive transport, the process starts with a need. The need can be the quest to conquer a new frontier in flight or simply do an existing transportation job better and more economically.

Technology is the most important ingredient in satisfying these needs. Some technology is already waiting in the laboratory, waiting for a "home" in a new aircraft. In other cases, technological barriers must be surmounted by additional work of scientists and engineers. The technology comes together in a complete aircraft that meets the original need. This whole process can take years—even decades, in the case of sophisticated military aircraft and commercial airliners. Thus, by looking at the technology now being developed and adding an insight into the needs of the future, a picture of the aircraft of the 21st century emerges.

In this book we will take this sequence—NEEDS, TECHNOLOGY, CONCEPTS—to predict the aircraft of the future. Because history is an important part in understanding the future, the book will start with a look at lessons that can be learned from the past.

While the theory and mathematics of flight can quickly become very complicated, the basic principles are usually quite simple to understand. We have attempted to explain the technology and concepts in terms that anyone with only an interest in aviation can comprehend.

1

Lessons From The Past

DECEMBER 17, 2003 will mark an important date in the history of man: the centennial of powered flight. Aviation has come a long way from the eventful day in 1903 when the Wright brothers proved man could fly. Before this 100th anniversary is celebrated, aviation will have progressed even further. This book will provide a look at these advances as well as give a glimpse of the aircraft that will be flying the skies in the year 2003, and you also will see some of the aviation technology that engineers and scientists are developing for use even further into the future.

PREDICTING THE FUTURE

Most of the advances in air travel have come about in an evolutionary manner with small steps forward rather than giant leaps. Indeed, the truly revolutionary discoveries like the jet engine, atomic energy, microchip, laser, and transistor are rare. Therefore, in many instances, predictions for the future can start with what is flying today and pro-

ject what evolutionary improvements will mean for the future.

Few concepts are totally new. Even the Wright brothers' early planes had a canard, pusher propeller, and tricycle landing gear—features considered modern today. You cannot thumb through too many early post-World War II issues of *Popular Mechanics* or *Popular Science* without coming across ideas for plastic airplanes. It took the development of sophisticated composites, however, to make the "plastic" airplane possible. Even the scramjet, the probable means of propelling the National Aerospace Plane, was fairly well developed during the 1960s before it fell into disfavor, mainly because of production difficulties and cost considerations. Some of the sneak previews of the Stealth bomber show flying-wing concepts that are reminiscent of the Northrop XB-35 and YB-49 flying wings of the 1940s (FIG. 1-1). In the future, you will see a revival of concepts from the past now made possible by advances in aerodynamics, materials, propulsion, electronics, and manufacturing technology.

Fig. 1-1. The Northrop flying wing was, perhaps, ahead of its time. However, it could appear again in the 21st century. This is a Northrop YB-49. (Courtesy Northrop Corporation)

Many of the advances in aerospace technology started with one man's invention. Take for example Frank Whittle's and Pabst von Ohain's jet engines, Michel Wibault's vectored-thrust engine, Robert Jones' scissor wing, Julian Wolkovitch's joined wing, or T. H. Maiman's laser. Today, scientists at universities and research laboratories are working on theories that will be the basis of aerospace systems of the future. Looking at their discoveries provides another insight into the future.

In the future, as in the past, the major burden of developing completely new aircraft will be borne by governments; in the United States this means the military services and the National Aeronautics and Space Administration (NASA). Their efforts will take on even greater importance as development costs are measured in billions of dollars. No private aerospace company, regardless of size, has the resources to take on many of the ambitious projects that could mean bankruptcy if unsuccessful. Some of the projects are so expensive that even governments will not be able to go it alone, resulting in partnerships between nations. This is not to say that all developments will be at the national or international level. There is still a place for individual breakthroughs promising financial rewards for companies, especially in the electronics, materials, and computer industries.

In the past, research aircraft like the X planes were used to try out new ideas before they were incorporated into production aircraft, usually military (TABLE 1-1). The military's and NASA's X planes of the 1940s and 1950s provided much information about flying at high altitudes and at transonic and supersonic speeds (FIG. 1-2). Other experimental aircraft, like the M2-F1/F2/F3, HL-10, and X-24A/B, were specifically built to investigate lifting body concepts (i.e., aircraft that obtain lift from their bodies rather than from conventional wings), and thus provided valuable data for the Space Shuttle. The world of Vertical/Short Takeoff and Landing (V/STOL) aircraft is filled with many experimental aircraft, like the XPY-1, X-13, XV-4A/B, and XV-3, that were less than unqualified successes (FIG. 1-3).

Today, building experimental aircraft strictly for research purposes has become prohibitive in cost. The only new X plane to come along in more than a decade is the Grumman X-29A that currently is investigating forward-sweep wing aerodynamics (FIG. 1-4). Other approaches have to be taken if new concepts are to be proven in actual flight.

Today's experimental aircraft are really highly modified versions of aircraft already in production. The U.S. Air Force's very successful Advanced Fighter Technology Integration (AFTI) program uses a highly modified General Dynamics F-16 *Fighting Falcon*. NASA recently used a variety of modified commercial and military transports for experimental platforms. For example, a Boeing 737 became a Terminal-Configured Vehicle (TCV) for studying ways to make landings safer, especially

Table 1-1. Significant Experimental Research Aircraft: The X Planes.

AIRCRAFT	MANUFACTURER	YEARS FLOWN	MAJOR GOAL	MAX. SPEED (MPH)	MAX. ALTITUDE (FT.)
D-558 I	Douglas	1947 - 1953	Investigate flight characteristics at transonic speeds	650.8	40,000
D-558 II	Douglas	1948 - 1956	Investigate swept-wing aircraft at high supersonic speeds	1291.0	83,235
X-3	Douglas	1952 - 1955	Investigate flight at sustained supersonic speeds	> Mach 1	41,318
X-1A/B/ D/E	Bell	1953 - 1958	Investigate flight at higher speeds and altitudes	1612.0	90,440
X-4	Northrop	1948 - 1953	Investigate semi-tailless aircraft at high subsonic speeds	620.0	40,000
X-5	Bell	1950 - 1954	Investigate aircraft capable of sweeping wings in flight	716.0	49,919
XF-92A	Convair	1951 - 1953	Investigate delta-wing aircraft at transonic speeds	Mach 1	42,464
X-15	North American	1959 - 1968	Investigate flight at very high speeds and altitudes	4520.0	354,200
X-29A	Grumman	1985 -	Investigate flight of forward-sweep aircraft	—	—
XB-70	North American	1965 - 1969	Investigate flight at high speeds	Mach 3	70,000

Fig. 1-2. The most famous of the X planes has to be the X-1A in which Chuck Yeager broke the sound barrier. (Courtesy Bell Aerospace Textron)

in bad weather. In the Aircraft Energy Efficiency (ACEE) program, modified air transports like the KC-135 and DC-10 have flight tested new aerodynamic, propulsion, and flight control ideas aimed at saving fuel.

Scale models are now being used to flight test new concepts. These range all the way from small radio controlled models, like the ones built by hobbyists, to ones that are manned. The revolutionary new Beech *Starship I* general-aviation aircraft made its first manned flight as an 85-percent scale model (FIG. 1-5), and the Fairchild T-46A, a concept for a new Air Force primary trainer, first flew at 62-percent scale.

Fig. 1-3. One of the many less-than-successful attempts at a V/STOL aircraft, the Bell X-22A. (Courtesy Bell Aerospace Textron)

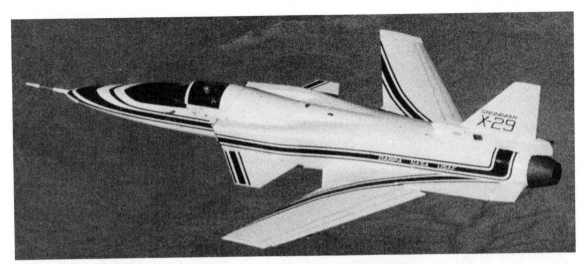

Fig. 1-4. The Grumman X-29 is the latest in the family of X planes. (Courtesy NASA)

Fig. 1-5. Flying scale models like this 85-percent scale model of the Beechcraft *Starship I* provide a relatively inexpensive way to flight test new aerodynamic designs. (Courtesy Beechcraft)

The use of remotely piloted research vehicles (RPRVs) offers almost unlimited promise as a way to flight test new concepts without the huge expense of man-rating research aircraft. One very successful example was the joint Air Force/NASA Highly Maneuverable Aircraft Technology (HiMat) craft that tested ideas that could be applied to high-performance fighter aircraft of the future (FIG. 1-6). Other RPRVs have been used during the development of the McDonnell Douglas F-15 and General Dynamics F-16 and to evaluate new V/STOL configurations.

Fig. 1-6. Remotely piloted research vehicles like this HiMat allow flight testing without the need for expensive man-rated aircraft. (Courtesy Rockwell International)

Computers are making great contributions in the development of new aircraft. Complete aircraft can be mathematically modeled on a computer, providing data that before could only be obtained from costly and time-consuming flight and wind-tunnel testing. Furthermore, changes to designs can be made simply by a few keystrokes or the movement of a light pen.

As in the past, much of the technology will filter down from the high-speed fighters to military and commercial transports. Some of this technology will even be incorporated into general-aviation craft, just as the jet engine (first used in fighters) became practical on transports like the deHavilland *Comet* and Boeing 707 and eventually on business jets like the Gates *Learjet* and Cessna *Citation.* Today, you can see some of the diffusion of technology in such things as composite materials used on aircraft like the AV-8 *Harrier* and now also being used on the Beechcraft *Starship I,* or the F-16's sidestick controller, now found in the cockpit of the Airbus Industrie A320 commercial airliner.

TRENDS FOR THE FUTURE

It is safe to say that there are no new physical frontiers in air travel. With the Space Shuttle, man has flown the entire flight envelope in terms of speed and altitude. Helicopters and V/STOL aircraft can fly forwards, backwards, sideways, and even stay suspended in mid-air. Aircraft have been flown in all sizes from the tiny man-powered ultralights to the giant Lockheed C-5 and Boeing 747. Incidentally, the last decade does not have a monopoly on aircraft size. Aircraft like the Sikorsky *Bolshoi* bomber (1913), Dornier *Do X* (1929), Messerschmitt *Gigant* (1941), and Saunders-Roe *Princess* (1962) were all huge aircraft.

So where do the challenges lie for the rest of this century and the next one? For military fighters and bombers, the key requirement will be the ability to survive in wartime and accomplish their missions in the face of an increasingly sophisticated enemy threat. This translates into things like great maneuverability, better defensive systems, and stealth technology. And future military designs

have to be reasonably economical to build and operate so they can be purchased and used in sufficient quantity.

While flying faster and with more people is of interest to the airlines, it only will happen if it means greater profits and can be done safely. Airlines have learned hard lessons about operating aircraft that are at the leading edge of the technology or have too much capacity. The jumbo jets and the supersonic transport (SST) are prime examples of this. Future airliners will be aimed at greater fuel efficiency, lower operating costs, and most importantly, safer flying. While you might see some exotic airliners like the hypersonic transport by the end of the 21st century, most air travel in the early part of the century will still be on airliners that look much like those used today. However, attached to (and within) rather conventional-looking fuselages will be an abundance of new materials, engines, electronics, and other items of high technology.

Advances in the expanding field of electronics will probably be the leading factor influencing future military and commercial transport aircraft. Lasers, computer-generated graphics, voice control, high-speed computer chips, and artificial intelligence will all play an important role. Space satellites will be used to get important weather and navigation information to pilots in real time and will become a key part of air traffic control, in skies that will become even more crowded. With all this information available to both military and commercial pilots, much thought will have to be given to equipment and techniques that reduce pilot workload.

General aviation encompasses everything that is not military or airline, including business aircraft, crop dusters, light and sport aircraft, and even ultralights and homebuilts. Today, business aircraft like the Beech *Starship I* and Avtek 400 are at the forefront of aircraft design and technology. New agricultural aircraft are being designed, and nowhere in aviation will you find a greater array of innovative designs than in the aircraft being assembled in basements and garages across America. For the private pilot, the upwardly spiraling cost of punching holes in the sky is a great problem. For aircraft flown mainly for pleasure, low initial and operating costs will be the driving force. Some of the technology developed for military and commercial aircraft will filter down to private aircraft, either as it becomes cheap enough or is mandated by safety regulations. Composites are already the mainstay of the homebuilder, and there are many lightplanes built decades ago that have sophisticated electronics retrofitted to their instrument panels.

Our prediction of the future begins by looking at the key technologies being developed in university, private, and government laboratories around the free world. Then we will look at various military, commercial, and general-aviation aircraft that will make use of this technology in the next half century.

Our look into the future will be limited to technologies and concepts that are possible and feasible based on current scientific knowledge. There will be no wild fantasies and no ideas that violate the laws of gravity, thermodynamics or nature. Some concepts, however, will be pushing these laws to their extremes. Any prediction of the future has to be caveated by the fact that we cannot forecast the effect of yet unknown breakthroughs in science. Who could have predicted, even twenty years ago, the effects that discoveries like the computer chip and laser would have on the world today?

AVIATION TECHNOLOGY TODAY

Before we begin our journey into the future, let us look at the current state of aerospace technology. This will provide a benchmark for measuring future progress. To do this, we will briefly examine the latest military, commercial, and general-aviation aircraft that are flying and see what new technologies they already are using. However, one word of caution here. While these aircraft might represent the latest things in the sky, their technologies are often dated. Because of the long lead time required to develop new aircraft, the technology they incorporate might be 5, 10, or more years old already, even though it was state-of-the-art when the design was frozen and the fabrication was started.

The General Dynamics F-16 *Fighting Falcon*. The F-16 is the U.S. Air Force's latest operational fighter, first flown in 1974 (FIG. 1-7). While advanced technology usually leads to a more costly and complex airplane, this was not the case here. The F-16 designers used advanced technology mainly where it would lead to a lighter weight, lower cost, and more effective fighting machine.

The F-16's blended-wing design (borrowed from the lifting-body spacecraft for returning to the Earth's atmosphere) provides more lift at high angles of attack, reduces drag, allows greater fuel capacity, and leads to a lighter and more rigid

Fig. 1-7. The General Dynamics F-16 *Fighting Falcon* is the newest fighter in the Air Force's inventory. (Courtesy U.S. Air Force)

structure. The "fly-by-wire" control system replaces bulky mechanical linkages, cables, and bell cranks with direct electrical commands transmitted via wires to individual actuators that move control surfaces. Many advances were made in the cockpit to improve pilot efficiency, especially during combat. The Head Up Display (HUD) presents vital information on the performance of aircraft systems on a transparent screen in front of the pilot.

The pilot can keep his eyes constantly on the world outside and does not need to even glance down to read his instruments. Replacing the normal fighter's joystick is a sidestick controller located conveniently at the pilot's right hand (FIG. 1-8). Sensing hand pressure rather than actual motion, the sidestick controller allows more precise maneuverability, especially under high G's. The pilot has an unobstructed view through an advanced plastic

Fig. 1-8. Sidestick controllers like the one on the right side of this F-16 cockpit will find their way into aircraft of the 21st century, including commercial airliners. (Courtesy General Dynamics)

Fig. 1-9. The AV-8 *Harrier* is the free world's first operational aircraft that takes off and lands horizontally and still flies like a fixed-wing aircraft. Indeed, the *Harrier* is able to approach the speed of sound. (Courtesy British Aerospace)

canopy that is virtually indestructible.

British Aerospace-McDonnell Douglas AV-8B *Harrier*. The AV-8B is the latest version of the free world's only operational V/STOL aircraft (FIG. 1-9). This fighter, flown by both the U.S. Marine Corps and British military forces, first flew in 1981. The original *Harrier* concept first flew back in 1960. The key technology that gives the *Harrier* its unique maneuverability, as well as letting it take off and land vertically, is vectored thrust. The four nozzles on the *Harrier's* jet engine can be rotated to provide thrust in the rearward, downward, or even forward direction.

The *Harrier* is the first combat aircraft to make extensive use of composite materials. Indeed, over 25 percent of the *Harrier II's* structure is made of graphite/epoxy. The AV-8B uses a supercritical wing design to obtain greater lift, more efficient cruise capability, and greater internal fuel capac-

ity. The cockpit is filled with modern electronics, like multicolor computer-generated displays on television-screen-like cathode-ray tubes (CRTs), and a Head Up Display.

British Aerospace - Aerospatiale *Concorde*. The *Concorde* is the only supersonic transport flying today (FIG. 1-10). Of the 14 *Concordes* built, only 11 are in service; British Airways flies seven and Air France flies four. Even though they were built prior to 1979 and based on technology that is now over a quarter-century old, *Concordes* are still advanced aircraft. They have to be, because they fly as fast as 1500 MPH, where the *Concorde's* tiny windows get as hot as oven doors and the fuselage actually stretches about nine inches. Not even military jets fly at supersonic speeds for as long as the *Concorde* does. The world's other two supersonic transports did not progress as well as the *Concorde*. The Soviets withdrew their TU-144

Fig. 1-10. The *Concorde* has proven that a supersonic transport is quite feasible even though it is currently used on very limited routes. (Courtesy British Aerospace)

from service after only a brief period of operation, and the domestic SST never got off the drawing board.

Airbus Industrie A300 Series. The *Airbus* represents the wave of the future in conventional commercial airliners (FIG. 1-11). Versions of this airliner, with seating capacities of 150 to 220 passengers, use composite materials in such areas as the tail fin. Its engines are designed for maximum fuel efficiency. The flight deck is the first of the "cockpits of the future," with such innovative features as a sidestick controller replacing the fa-

miliar control yoke and a complete Electronic Flight Instrument System (EFIS) that displays information on multipurpose computer screens. Later models will incorporate a fly-by-wire control system.

Beechcraft *Starship I.* This new business jet is as modern as its name implies. For starters, its fuselage and wings are made almost entirely of composite materials (FIG. 1-12). The advanced aerodynamic design includes a variable geometry (i.e., a movable forward wing or canard) and large tipsails at the ends of the main wing. These fea-

Fig. 1-11. The Airbus Industrie A310-300 represents the latest in commercial airliners. (Courtesy Airbus Industrie)

11

Fig. 1-12. The Beechcraft *Starship I* offers a wide cabin despite relatively narrow external dimensions. Thin composite walls make this possible. (Courtesy Beechcraft)

tures reduce drag and improve directional stability.

The *Starship's* twin-pusher "jetfans" combine the best features of the propjet, fanjet, and propfan engines. Sitting in front of the many CRTs on the instrument panel, you get the feeling you are flying the Space Shuttle rather than a business aircraft.

=2=

Needs Of
The Future

THERE IS A SAYING in the aerospace world: "requirements push and technology pulls." What this means is that the requirements of new missions, or even the need to do current jobs better, drive engineers and scientists to work on the leading edge of technology (FIG. 2-1). They have to find solutions to problems posed by more demanding requirements through the invention and development of new ideas and technology. On the other side of the coin, new concepts are constantly being invented in university, government, and commercial laboratories. It takes forward-thinking planners to envision how these new technologies can be used for improving military and civilian aerospace capabilities and to actually develop new aircraft around these breakthroughs in technology. This is how "technology pulls."

This chapter examines the missions and jobs military and civilian aircraft must do in the future and presents the requirements for advancing technology. Subsequent chapters will cover the technology being pursued to produce aircraft that can

meet these requirements, as well as new technology that could result in aircraft and capabilities as yet unimagined.

MILITARY MISSIONS

Military missions place the greatest demands on technology. This is easily seen by the vast sums of money required to develop new weapons systems like the Rockwell B-1 bomber and the Air Force's Advanced Tactical Fighter (ATF) (FIG. 2-2). Even a relatively unsophisticated aircraft like the C-17 airlift transport represents a rather large investment.

The U.S. Air Force, Navy, Army, and Marine Corps are assigned a variety of missions that must be conducted from the air, or at least require support from airborne craft. The Air Force is naturally the "big gun" in the aerospace world, with missions ranging from strategic bombing and air-to-air combat to transporting vast numbers of troops anywhere in the world on a moment's notice. Added

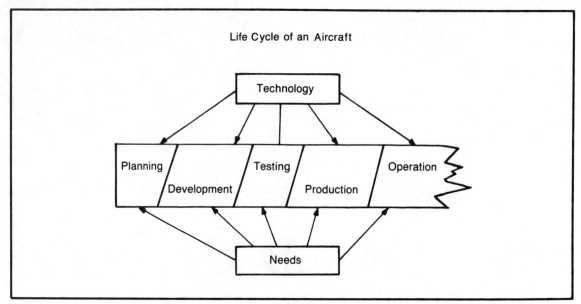

Fig. 2-1. An aircraft's life cycle, from initial conception to retirement in the boneyard, can last decades. The development of a new airplane, especially a military craft, can last 10 or even 20 years. And as experience with aircraft like the B-52 and C-130 has shown, a basic design might be in operation for a half-century or more.

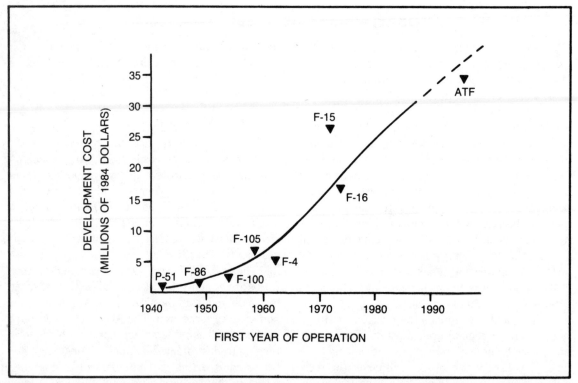

Fig. 2-2. Aircraft costs have grown drastically through the years. This shows the flyaway costs for typical Air Force fighters.

to this are the important jobs of reconnaissance and surveillance.

The Navy's air requirements are focused on defense of its fleet, protection of the submarine force, protection of naval power ashore, and supporting of U.S. naval forces around the world. Both the Air Force and Navy are tasked to give close air support to troops fighting on the ground.

The Army's aircraft needs are centered around direct support of the ground troops. Thus, the Army relies heavily on rotorcraft for attacking targets, transporting troops in the field, and keeping troops supplied. Except for the jobs of strategic bombing and reconnaissance, Marine Corps aviation does what the Air Force, Navy, and Army do, but on a somewhat more limited scale.

Bombers. The question often comes up: Does the U.S. really need expensive strategic bombers when it has very capable land-based intercontinental ballistic missiles (ICBMs) like the Minuteman (and eventually the MX) as well as the Navy's submarine-launched ballistic missiles (SLBMs) like the Trident? The answer is a resounding yes, as long as the U.S. maintains its strategic deterence policy based on Triad.

In simple terms, Triad is the use of ICBMs, SLBMs, and strategic bombers as a three-prong deterrence to any Soviet thought of nuclear aggression. Each of the three Triad elements contributes its own unique threat to the Soviet Union as a result of its individual characteristics and means of deployment. Because of these distinct differences, Triad represents an enormous threat to the Russians, one that takes a tremendous expenditure of national resources to counter (if, indeed, each component can even be defended against to a satisfactory degree). The Soviets must invest heavily in a variety of detection and counterforce technologies, just as the U.S. wants them to do.

From an American standpoint, Triad represents a hedge against any breakthrough in Soviet technology that might degrade one of the Triad components. If one component is negated, the other two can fill in the gap until American technology overcomes the deficiency. It is very unlikely that the Soviets can come up with breakthroughs that

could degrade all three elements simultaneously. The U.S., in other words, has not put all of its deterrence in one basket.

What then is the strategic bomber's contribution to Triad? Foremost, it is the only one of the three components that can be recalled after launch. It can be used as a show of power and recalled before actually inflicting damage. It is flexible in the sense that its designated targets can be changed while the aircraft is en route, an impossibility with both the ICBM and SLBM, whose targets are programmed prior to launch. Finally, the bomber is the only one of the three that can be used for other missions, such as non-nuclear, conventional bombing in limited war situations (as was done with the B-52 during the Vietnam conflict).

Today, the bomber's job is not an easy one, considering the advanced state of the Soviets' detection systems and the ability of their anti-aircraft weapons, interceptors, and surface-to-air missiles to destroy bombers—thus, the need for "low observables," or stealth technology, to allow U.S. bombers to penetrate enemy defenses.

In the past, the philosophy used with the B-52, and now planned for the B-1, was to use varying speeds and altitudes plus sophisticated electronic countermeasures (ECM), electronic counter-countermeasures (ECCM) and electronic warfare (EW) techniques to defeat enemy anti-bomber defenses. The new stealth philosophy will make the bomber "invisible" so it cannot be seen by any of the enemy's sensors. This means reducing radar, infrared, and other signatures to their absolute minimums. ECM and ECCM equipment would still be on board, but would be mainly for the final phase of the mission when the threat of detection would be the greatest.

The topic of low observables will not be limited to bombers alone, but will be found on the list of specifications for just about every military aircraft. Although they might not require the technological sophistication needed for bombers and interceptors, future helicopters and transports will be designed with low visible, acoustic, thermal, and radar signatures.

Interceptors. The interceptor, the aircraft of

"dogfight" fame, will still be around in the 21st century, not only engaging enemy fighters, but also defending against bombers and missile attacks. It, too, will become very sophisticated in order to do its job. Stealth technology will be as important here as for the strategic bomber. The interceptor will require even greater maneuverability if it is to survive attacks from enemy air- and ground-launched missiles.

One of the things of concern to military planners today is the ability to take off and land aircraft, including interceptors, on airfields that are severely damaged during wartime (FIG. 2-3 AND PLATE 10). Aircraft of all types will probably have to operate from bomb-cratered runways, right from the outset, in any future war. This means aircraft should require a minimum of real estate, something the Navy already knows about from its carrier-based operations.

The myriad of sensors aboard future aircraft will provide the pilot with a vast amount of information, not only about what is happening with his aircraft, but also about the combat arena outside. Perhaps, the pilot will be confronted with too much data. In a single-pilot, high-speed aircraft, the pilot must first *aviate,* that is, fly the aircraft on course and maneuver as required. Second, he must *navigate* so he knows where he is, where he is going, and how to get there. Then he must *communicate,* receiving and transmitting information while in the air. Finally, he must *operate,* that is, manage and use all his defensive and offensive systems, acquire and track targets, and fire his weapons. In the heat of battle, he must be able to do this with split-second accuracy. This multitude of simultaneous tasks would overload even the best pilot. Thus, there is a great requirement for reducing pilot workload through the use of high technology, especially in single-seat, high-performance aircraft.

Close Air Support. All four military services are called upon to provide close air support to ground troops. The Air Force, Navy, and Marine Corps use fixed-wing aircraft for this role, while the Army and Marine Corps use helicopters for ground-support work.

The close-air-support fighter requirements also include low observables and the ability to operate from damaged runways, and for the Navy and Marines Corps, from ships with flight decks much smaller than a typical aircraft carrier.

The ideal close-support fighter is one that can operate from airfields or ships located near the forward edge of the battle area (FEBA). The idea is to have aircraft that can quickly fly back to support bases for re-arming and refueling and return to the thick of battle within minutes. This implies the need for vertical/short takeoff and landing capability. Because ground battles will continue in the worst of weather and at night, the close-support fighter must have all-weather and night fighting capability.

The close-support aircraft must also be survivable. First, it must be able to avoid detection. That is where low observables come into play. Then, if it is detected, it must be able to survive hits from enemy fire, mainly in the form of small-arms fire. The aircraft must be able to fly home with battle damage and then be easily repaired for a quick return to combat. Finally, if he is going to be able to fight effectively, the ground-support pilot will require assistance in handling his tremendous workload.

Airlift Transports. Airlift transports are the very large aircraft needed to carry large contingents of troops and their fighting equipment anywhere in the world where the U.S. wants to project a military presence, or needs to engage in battle. Not only must these aircraft be able to carry large tonnage, they must be able to load, carry, and unload outsize cargo, such as the tanks, helicopters, and howitzers that are a part of the modern store of Army weapons. High subsonic cruising speeds are desirable in airlift transports in order to get the maximum number of troops to a trouble spot in the minimum amount of time.

Assault Transports. Whereas the airlift transports get the troops and equipment to the general region of combat, the assault transport must take these men and gear to the exact point

Fig. 2-3. Opposite: Military aircraft will have to operate from severely damaged runways in future wars. (Courtesy McDonnell Douglas)

on the battlefield where they are needed. This can be done by airborne assault using paratroops, or by landing and unloading right on the battlefield. In any case, the assault transport must be able to operate from the most primitive runways—airstrips that will usually be damaged. It must also be essentially self-sufficient, requiring no ground support equipment or ground-based navigation aids. Naturally, survivability in combat is a requirement.

Reconnaissance and Surveillance. Space satellites perform reconnaissance and surveillance today, but there will always be a need for "spy" aircraft that fly in the atmosphere, or at least at its very fringes. Cloud obscuration, poor weather, and the laws of orbital mechanics sometimes mean that needed information cannot always be obtained from orbiting spacecraft. High- and fast-flying reconnaissance aircraft must be ready to do the job. Because these aircraft will have to fly over enemy territory without being detected, stealth technology is a must.

Tactical reconnaissance and surveillance for actual combat operations is very time-critical because of the fluidity of the modern battlefield. The military cannot rely totally on satellite information, but must send in reconnaissance aircraft to obtain information on enemy positions, buildups, and electronic order of battle. The tactical reconnaissance aircraft must have low observables and be able to survive enemy action. It must also be able to operate from primitive and battle-damaged airfields.

Because many reconnaissance and surveillance missions are quite dangerous, they might best be performed by unmanned drones and remotely piloted vehicles (RPVs). RPVs can be much less expensive than manned aircraft and are expendable in time of war.

Aircraft that are half airplane and half space satellite are also generating interest. These ultra-high-altitude, unmanned craft can fly for weeks—or perhaps even months—at a time, with very low fuel consumption or the ability to fly on solar power.

Trainers. Sometimes forgotten are the aircraft needed to train new military pilots. These range all the way from primary and basic trainers used to teach fledgling aviators, to advanced trainers used for combat practice. For initial instruction, a trainer must be safe and economical to operate, as well as represent the type of aircraft the trainee will eventually be flying. The aircraft must be rather forgiving of student mistakes and able to take a lot of punishment, yet be able to perform high-performance aerobatics. These trainers must also sip fuel and require minimum maintenance, even though they accumulate flight hours very rapidly.

Advanced training for multi-seat aircraft can be accomplished in the aircraft themselves. Training for high-performance, single-seat aircraft is done in dual-seat versions of the particular airplane (e.g., tandem-seat versions of the F-16 *Fighting Falcon* and AV-8 *Harrier*).

In the future, more training will be done in craft that never leave the ground, that is, in simulators. They provide far less expensive training and can create situations that could never be attempted in a real airplane. The key requirement for simulators is realism, which places great demands on the computers that are the heart of the simulator.

Space Launcher. The 21st century will see a replacement for the Space Shuttle. The emphasis will be on an aircraft-like launcher that can reduce the cost of placing payloads in orbit. A low-cost launch vehicle is a must if the U.S. is to undertake such ambitious programs as a manned space station or the various orbital platforms that would be part of the Strategic Defensive Initiative ("Star Wars"). One of the ways launch costs can be reduced is through the use of a launcher that can use regular jet aircraft runways rather than the specialized launch pads at Cape Canaveral or Vandenberg AFB. Another goal is airplane-like turnaround times between launches.

A space launcher that will fly at a speed of Mach 25 presents great demands on technology, in terms of aerodynamics, propulsion, electronics, structures, and materials. This same technology could be used to build hypersonic bombers, interceptors, and reconnaissance aircraft, as well as hypersonic airliners that could cut trips halfway around the world to a few hours.

Rotorcraft. Rotorcraft, meaning helicopters

and hybrid aircraft that combine the features of both the helicopter and fixed-wing aircraft, offer unique military capabilities. Vietnam is often referred to as the "Helicopter War" because of the tremendous contributions made by helicopters like the Bell-built *Huey* transports and gunships. The future of the combat helicopter is very promising in light of the need to operate near the FEBA, often from completely destroyed runways. Added to this is the helicopter's unique ability to fly nap-of-the-Earth amongst trees and rocks to avoid detection. The helicopter not only can land troops on the battlefield, but can return to extract them when the mission is over or when a retreat is ordered.

The helicopter has several shortcomings that will push technology. One of these is top speed, which is limited to about 200 knots for a pure helicopter. Thus, the need exists for rotorcraft that also use other means (besides rotors) for high-speed flight. Such devices might also improve another deficit of the helicopter, its range.

Because the helicopter has to work so close to the enemy, low observables and survivability against enemy action represent acute problems. While great progress has already been made in reducing the infrared, radar, visible, and the difficult acoustic signature of the helicopter, there is still much work to be done to achieve an "invisible" and "silent" helicopter. Other goals for future helicopter designs include increased payload capacity, reduced maintenance requirements, less vibration, and reduced pilot workload.

An interesting new mission is appearing on the horizon for the helicopter: an anti-helicopter function. Someday dogfights between missile- and gun-armed helicopters are inevitable. This will not only require developing tactics, but also advancing technology, especially improving maneuverability and survivability.

Feasibility vs. Affordability. While all sorts of new concepts and applications of technology are feasible, they are not all economically possible. First, there is the cost of development; some of the ideas would be much too expensive for America. Then there is the matter of life-cycle costs—not only the original development cost, but

the cost of buying operational aircraft and operating them on a day-to-day basis for decades. These operational costs can often far outshadow original development and procurement investments. Two of the high-ticket items here are fuel costs and maintenance expense. Future technology advances are needed in the less glamorous, but highly important, propulsion and ease-of-maintenance technologies.

COMMERCIAL AIR PASSENGER SERVICE

Military aircraft designs are driven by military mission requirements, and while the cost to buy and operate is important, it is not the paramount consideration. For commercial aircraft, profitability is a major consideration, as is safety. Other factors are really of lesser importance.

The universal parameter used by airlines in evaluating profitability is the direct operating cost per seat mile. The greatest cost of running an airline today is the cost of fuel. Fortunately, this cost can be reduced by advances in technology, if the cost savings are not outweighed by the investment required. To keep investments within bounds, many techniques to reduce fuel usage are rather simple ones, especially in comparison to technologies needed for military aircraft (e.g., stealth requirements). Fuel savings can come from more efficient engines, so there will be much emphasis on improving engine efficiency in the years to come. Fuel savings can also result from lower-drag designs as well as simple techniques like keeping an airplane's fuselage and wings clean. A NASA study showed that a dirty Lockheed L-1011 could cost as much as $100,000 more per year to operate than a clean one—and that was when jet fuel was only 32 cents per gallon. Making aircraft lighter, such as by using composite materials, is another fuel-saving technique.

While not as dramatic as the effect of reduced fuel costs, lower personnel costs are also of interest to the airlines, particularly by reducing the size of maintenance crews and flight crews. Advances in electronics, computers, and artificial intelligence could make a single-pilot airliner quite feasible, and indeed, even make a robotically flown aircraft possible. It is unlikely, however, that either of these will ever become reality; passengers will probably never feel comfortable unless at least two pilots man the cockpit. On a more positive note, future technology from military aircraft will find its way into the commercial airliner cockpit to reduce pilot workload, so pilots can cope with flying in increasingly crowded skies.

Another way to improve profitability is to increase the number of seats on airliners, but this is more easily said than done. From past experience with jets like the Boeing 747, there are only a few routes in the world which generate profitable passenger load factors for jumbo airliners. While some visionaries project aircraft with seating capacities of 600 or 700 passengers, these will probably never materialize. For one thing, the huge development and purchase costs cannot be amortized on those few profitable routes unless the aircraft are also used extensively for cargo-carrying duties. For the most part, airlines prefer the flexibility of smaller aircraft. Also, while seldom mentioned, the adverse publicity that would be generated by the loss of life in the crash of a 500- to 700-passenger aircraft is another consideration.

Because of the huge cost of developing entirely new airliners, we will see current airliners used well into the 21st century, although some of these are likely to be updated with new engines and minor aerodynamic changes to improve their efficiency. It is quite possible that some airframes will be used for a half-century, albeit with modifications and improvements.

The new airliners rolling off the assembly lines in the next few decades will be evolutionary models of those airliners now in operation. Do not expect any radical changes in subsonic airliner designs. Most people feel comfortable and safe flying in aircraft they are familiar with and that have built up safe and reliable records over millions of passenger-miles.

Many of the requirements for more economical, more efficient, and safer airliners will be satisfied by incorporating advances in computer and electronic technology. Such things as computerized engine and flight controls, as well as a myriad of high-technology communications, navigation, and safety devices, will help meet the airlines' needs for improved operations within their financial constraints. Electronics can often be installed on aircraft by adding a few black-boxes and rerouting of wiring. Some technology improvements require only the rewriting of computer software. This does not imply, however, that all electronic technology developments come cheaply. They still require significant investments for research, development, testing, and certification.

If you take a casual look into the future, your conclusion might be that aircraft of the 21st century will fly faster; indeed, some experts think they will fly at hypersonic speeds. This premise deserves a closer look, especially from a bottom-line economics standpoint.

There is no getting around the fact that faster airplanes are more costly to build and operate. When you fly at supersonic speeds, more sophisticated propulsion systems, materials, flight controls, and just about everything else are needed, and costs jump—sometimes by an order of magnitude. But where the costs really rise is in day-to-day operations. Engines guzzle tremendous amounts of fuel at supersonic speeds, and maintenance becomes much more complex because of the stresses and temperatures put on exotic materials.

All of this means that a fairly stiff premium must be paid by passengers who want to save a few hours in the air. As witnessed by British Airways' and Air France's experience with the *Concorde,* there are only a few routes in the world where there is sufficient passenger interest in paying a steep surcharge. The *Concorde* now only flies from London and Paris to New York, Washington, and Miami; the original plans for Concorde showed it covering the globe. One reason is that supersonic flights over many countries, most significantly the United States, are prohibited because of sonic boom problems. This means that supersonic flights are constrained mainly to transoceanic routes. The removal of these restrictions is highly unlikely, because of the political and environmental considerations. Development of hypersonic airliners that fly at the fringes of the atmosphere would be a very expensive solution.

Another consideration often overlooked, is the frequency and convenience of flights. Saving two or three hours inflight is of little value to the busy executive if he or she must lose several hours because the airline's schedule does not fit the executive's schedule. Likewise, time gained en route can be quickly lost if connecting flights mean long delays or if long-distance ground travel must be made to get to the selected airports where ultra-high-speed flights originate and terminate.

You should not conclude, however, that supersonic and hypersonic airliners will not be developed for the 21st century. But they do present a much more difficult challenge if they are to be profitable.

In the next few decades, people will be traveling greater distances more routinely. The interweaving of business and commercial interests on a global basis will require long-distance business travel, especially in the far-flung Pacific region. Added to this is a projected increase in pleasure travel and an increase in the affluent retired population. High speed aircraft are one way to reduce travel times. Another less-technologically-demanding approach is the development of longer-range aircraft that can reduce travel times by eliminating intermediate refueling stops.

Yet another way to reduce travel times is to reduce time spent in getting to and from airports, in boarding and disembarking, and in retrieving luggage. Then there is the time lost while in the holding pattern or waiting for takeoff clearance. Added to these are the security delays brought about by acts of terrorism that will, unfortunately, probably not diminish in the future. Solutions to these problems represent real payoffs in reducing travel time. But they are the most challenging problems airlines and airport operators have to face, indeed, more difficult than developing a faster airliner. And these problems will increase as airports and airways become even more congested.

Costs are not the only problems facing airlines today and in the future. High technology will be required to make air travel safer through improved traffic control, mid-air-collision avoidance systems,

and instrumentation for flights in poor weather conditions. Airlines are already aware of the pressure of environmental groups to alleviate noise and air pollution around airports.

Another important aspect of air travel is the short-hop commuter business. While air transportation already accounts for almost all long-distance travel (at least in the U.S.), commuter airlines must compete with ground transportation, especially the automobile. Today, distances of about 200 miles or less are most efficiently and cost effectively covered by car. To capture this segment of the market, air terminals must be built near city centers. This will require that advanced concepts, such as V/STOL aircraft, be pursued. Ironically, the poor fuel economy and high noise levels of V/STOL aircraft present another technology challenge.

In the past half century, the airline industry has seen an almost exponential increase in passengers, along with reduced travel times. At the same time, the cost of air travel has decreased continually. If inflation and the ever-decreasing buying power of the dollar are factored in, the decrease in the cost of air travel is really dramatic. In the future, both the speed and capacity of airliners will remain essentially constant. The challenge will be in keeping fares as low as possible while still earning a fair profit for the airlines. What will dramatically change, however, is the total volume of passengers carried by air. This will present a challenge in terms of the ability to safely handle a much larger amount of traffic, both in the air and on the ground.

COMMERCIAL AIR CARGO SERVICE

Air cargo traffic will grow also, especially if air shipping costs can be made competitive with trucks, trains, and for overseas destinations, surface ships. Unlike airlines, cargo carriers could reduce costs through the use of very large aircraft. Not only would the cargo transporters be able to economically transport a large volume of freight on a single flight, but they could carry oversized items like construction equipment and heavy manufacturing machinery.

To air cargo carriers, volume and weight carrying capacity are often more important than maximum speed. One interesting possibility is a large aircraft capable of carrying both cargo and passengers. Aircraft designed like the Air Force's C-5, in which people are carried on the top deck and cargo below, could be very profitable for service even to the more remote areas of the world.

In order to operate ultra-large transports, major changes in the ground handling of cargo will be required. Efficient methods will have to be devised to quickly load and unload large volumes of freight. Also to save time, airports designed strictly for handling large airfreighters could be built away from congested passenger terminals. There is no point to shipping by air if the time is lost on the ground. This is an especially important factor if air transport is to be competitive with trucking in the United States.

Because airports to service ultra-large transports would require large tracts of land and because a bulk of their flights would originate and terminate at coastal cities, seaplanes might be a very logical solution. You might see large flying boats, modern versions of the giants that opened up transoceanic flight in the 1930s and early 1940s.

In the past, freight carriers used cast-off airliners, but with the advent of highly profitable and efficient air-express overnight services, things have really changed. The requirements of these carriers could have a major impact on the commercial air transport industry in the future. As the term "express" implies, these carriers' unique service is based on speed. Overnight delivery anywhere in the U.S. is the rule, and now one-day service is available to Europe. Transpacific routes are next on the agenda. Indeed, today's high-technology industries are highly dependent on the express carrier. Now it is not necessary to maintain large inventories of products or replacement parts in various locations. With air express they can be maintained at a single location, reducing inventory and facility costs.

Because of its need for speed, the air-express carrier could be the first commercial user of a new supersonic, or even a hypersonic, transport to provide overnight service just about anywhere in the world. Studies have already shown that even *Concorde* could produce about three times the revenue by carrying high-priority packages compared to hauling passengers.

But speed is not the only ingredient that has made the air-express business what it is today. Absolute reliability is why most customers use the express carriers. If a passenger airliner is late or canceled, a few hundred people might be inconvenienced. A cancelled air-express flight could mean tens of thousands of critical items would not get there when they were "absolutely, positively" needed. Production lines—even whole companies—could be shut down for the lack of key electronic or computer parts. To meet schedules, air-express carriers must fly in all types of weather—rain, snow, fog, and especially darkness. Overnight delivery means lots of night flying; the required capabilities are almost like those needed for the military's all-weather fighters.

The air-express carriers could profitably use the super-large airfreighter, especially for future transoceanic operations. Because passengers are not involved, landings and takeoffs could take place from isolated airfields or, most likely, from seaports; such a large aircraft would probably be a flying boat. The aircraft would be designed for rapid loading and unloading, so that packages could be quickly transferred to smaller aircraft for continuation to their final destinations.

At the other end of the scale, the air-express carriers could benefit from V/STOL aircraft. These could provide rapid intercity transport, avoiding congested airport facilities. They have the advantage over helicopters in both speed and range. A V/STOL could fly hundreds of miles each night, landing and taking off from small terminals on the outskirts of towns.

GENERAL AVIATION

General aviation can be divided into two categories, flying done for commercial purposes (other than the major airlines and freight carriers discussed above) and flying done just for the fun of it. In the first category there are the crop dusters, business and executive transports, aircraft used in the offshore petroleum industry, plus a multitude of other uses that are best served by light aircraft. In the second category are the aircraft used for personal transport and pleasure flying.

The general aviation industry currently is depressed for a variety of reasons, so there are some real challenges for the next few decades. Again, economics is a driving factor. Buying and operating a light aircraft is out of the reach of many people who, in the past, could have afforded an airplane just to "punch holes in the clouds." Light aircraft prices have soared from about the price of a luxury car to the price of an expensive home, or even more. The cost of certification and spiraling liability insurance premiums, as well as the multitude of electronics required to fly in today's crowded skies, are the major contributors to these dramatic price increases. While advanced technology can help drive down costs, the significant changes needed to save the general-aviation industry will probably not come from the drawing board and laboratory, but from changes in laws and regulations.

One way the aviation buff can keep flying is through the use of ultralights and homebuilts. Interestingly, these low-cost aircraft are developing some advanced technology of their own, especially in the areas of aerodynamics and materials. Some of this technology might flow upstream; the homebuilts offer a very inexpensive way to try out new ideas.

When it comes to general-aviation aircraft, not only is the cost of fuel important, but so is its availability. Light aircraft will use reciprocating engines for many years into the future. In the past, these engines were designed to burn specially blended avgas. For a variety of reasons, the petroleum industry has drastically reduced the sale of avgas and eventually will eliminate it completely. Future light aircraft engines will be designed to get by on the same gasoline as the family car. Research is also being done on aircraft engines that burn diesel fuel, liquid petroleum gas, and jet fuels.

Because of airspace congestion and the concern for safety in the skies, aircraft electronics, or *avionics,* have become very sophisticated and expensive. Some of these devices are mandated by

the Federal Aviation Administration; others are optional but highly desirable. The challenge for the electronics industry is to design and build "black boxes" that the average aviation enthusiast can afford.

One of the largest single users of helicopters is the offshore petroleum industry. As offshore oil rigs move farther offshore to service new oil fields, the time involved in commuting to and from them by helicopter will become excessive and too expensive, especially when crews are paid "portal-to-portal." The answer will probably be V/STOL aircraft.

SOVIET AVIATION

What are the Soviets planning in the way of aircraft for the 21st century? Because the Soviets are tight-lipped on their plans, detailed projections are impossible to present here. Indeed, the Central Intelligence Agency and the military services have buildings full of experts who do nothing but attempt to ferret out Soviet aviation plans, technology, and concepts of the future, and their conclusions are highly classified. However, using information about Soviet technology of the past, their needs and requirements, plus an understanding of how their aerospace "industry" is organized and how it functions, we can come up with some trends for future Soviet aircraft designs (FIG. 2-4).

To set the record straight, contrary to what is sometimes believed, the Soviets do not merely copy our technology and designs. They have a very large pool of talented engineers and scientists, estimated to be much larger than in the U.S., who are quite capable of designing and developing aircraft to meet unique Soviet military and commercial requirements.

One reason Soviet designs might look like those of the free world is that the same laws of nature apply in the USSR as in the rest of the world. Soviet engineers start with the same laws of physics, aerodynamics, thermodynamics, and so forth. Area ruling, swept wings, drag divergence, and thrust vectoring work the same in Leningrad and Stalingrad as they do in Los Angeles and Seattle.

Secondly, the requirements placed on aircraft

are quite similar. While military strategy and tactics might differ in detail, Soviet aircraft still must be able to survive in combat to complete their missions.

In the past, the emphasis was on quantity versus quality, but that is changing. Threats to the Soviets from the free world are becoming so sophisticated that simple aircraft and systems annot do the job. Also, the cost of developing and operating aircraft is growing just as rapidly there as in the rest of the world. For example, fuel availability is becoming of more concern to the Soviets, so they will have to use jet engines that are more efficient than the simple, fuel-gulping engines of years past. Other factors, like the need for reliable systems with a minimum of maintenance, reduced pilot workload in the heat of battle, and problems of detectibility and survivability against ground threats, are also being studied by Soviet engineers.

The Soviets are making greater use of advanced technology in the aircraft now coming into their inventory, and the trend will increase in the future. They have their own V/STOL fighter, the YAK-36 *Forger,* and they appear to be working at the extreme limit of the flight envelope with a version of a hypersonic aircraft.

Naturally, the Soviets are not averse to incorporating free-world technology obtained through overt or covert sources when it suits their needs and allows them to leapfrog current designs without expensive and time-consuming research and development. An example of this is the An-72 transport that bears more than a casual resemblance to the Boeing YC-14, which never reached production. Of course, U.S. aerospace companies and their military and civilian customers would not be bashful about "borrowing" a good idea from the Soviets.

One of the main factors that cause Soviet and free-world aircraft design philosophies to differ is the difference in ideologies. Soviet aircraft are designed under a very tightly controlled and centralized bureaucratic government. There is no real competition between aerospace companies and no need to satisfy the public through a congress or parliament. There are also no critical news media to expose shortcomings. The Soviet bureaucracy, however, is perhaps an even greater impediment to progress; the fear of failure is a constant one and leads to conservatism in designs. In most instances, the Soviets do not use advanced technology in their designs until it is totally proven. The key in Soviet designs is evolution versus revolution. But never sell the Soviet aircraft short. They are well built to carry out their intended missions.

Soviet aircraft are designed by design bureaus assigned responsibility for a particular type of aircraft. For example, Sukhoi designs interceptors and ground-attack fighters, Tupolev designs bombers, MiG designs fighters, Antonov designs transports, and Mil designs helicopters. Once an aircraft design is ready to go into production, it is turned over to a manufacturing institute. The design bureaus are just that, design bureaus. While this results in great economy of resources, it tends to smother original and unique ideas.

In years past, the Soviets put great emphasis on building prototypes of aircraft before putting them into production. The design bureaus would build alternative prototypes to meet a given requirement and then pick the best one through a flyoff competition. This paralleled similar practices in the U.S., such as the competition between the McDonnell Douglas YF-16 and the Northrop YF-17. However, just as in the U.S., the expense of building and testing Soviet prototypes is becoming too great. This is another indication of how far Soviet aircraft have advanced in complexity and expense.

One of the unique features of the Soviet research and development process is the handbook method of design. For example, the Soviets' Central Aero-Hydrodynamic Bureau does research in various aerospace disciplines, the results of which are incorporated into design handbooks. These handbooks are used by the engineers in the design bureaus who actually design aircraft that will be manufactured. Handbooks are another factor leading to conservatism in Soviet aircraft designs.

Now that you have a basic understanding of aviation needs of the future, let us predict how they will be satisfied.

3

Aerodynamics

AERODYNAMICS determine the overall appearance of an aircraft. However, unlike products such as automobiles or refrigerators, every part of an aircraft's external styling has a specific purpose. Nothing, except for (perhaps) the paint job, is there just because it looks good. On some aircraft even the paint is chosen to perform a specific function, such as to reduce aircraft temperatures or to make it difficult for the enemy to detect.

In the early days of aviation, the pioneers only had a rudimentary understanding of aerodynamics, and the designs were mostly the result of intuition and trial-and-error. Today, aerodynamics is a highly developed science, and aircraft designs are the result of extensive testing in both the wind tunnel and on the computer. In the future, the computer will have an even more significant impact on the aerodynamic design of aircraft. With ultrahigh-speed computers, the designer can try out new designs simply by making a few changes with a light pen on a computer screen. Expensive wind-tunnel models and flight testing will only be needed to evaluate the final designs.

The aerodynamics of a particular aircraft are determined by the aircraft's purpose. Optimum performance, whether it be maximum speed or altitude, or now the important consideration of fuel economy, is largely determined by an aircraft's aerodynamics. Of course, pure aerodynamic designs have to be tempered by the fact that an aircraft must have engines to propel it, and must be able to carry people or cargo and to land and take off. Through the years, inventors have come up with great proposals for aircraft designs that never went into production, either because they were too difficult or expensive to build, or because there were no materials available that could withstand the stress of flight over years of operation. As you will see, some of these rather "way-out" ideas of the past will be possible in the future because of the major strides being made in materials and manufacturing technologies.

WINGS

When you look at any aircraft, the thing that probably strikes you first is the design of the wings, the components that provide most of the aircraft's lift. Future aircraft will use many wing designs that are already proven and in operation on current aircraft. But they will also use some advanced ideas that will greatly enhance performance.

Flying Wing

Because wings are what give an airplane lift, and just about every other part of the airframe contributes only drag (at least from an aerodynamicist's point of view), why not build an aircraft that only has wing surfaces—a flying wing?

That is what Northrop and the Air Force did with designs like the piston-powered XB-35 and jet-powered YB-49 of the 1940s. Jack Northrop conceived the flying wing, determining that if the entire weight of the aircraft was spread along the wingspan, the aircraft would be more aerodynamically efficient. With a flying wing, the weight is where the lift is, and the large bending forces found in conventional aircraft are eliminated. The wing, therefore, can have a very large span. The flying wing also eliminates much of the parasitic drag generated by a fuselage.

Although both flying-wing bomber designs flew successfully, for several reasons neither went into production. The YB-49 was slower than the Boeing B-47 (which the Air Force eventually purchased), and without a major redesign, it could not carry the large nuclear weapons in use at the time.

Another difficulty was controlling the flying wing in flight. Limited tail control, due to the lack of the typical tail surfaces located at the end of a long fuselage, gave severe problems in lateral, longitudinal, and directional stability. The control systems of the day were not advanced enough to compensate for the limited tail control. Today, computerized stability-augmentation systems are up to the task. Because of both their structural efficiency and reduced drag, flying wings are of interest again, especially in very large cargo transports where huge quantities of cargo could be carried in the wings (FIG. 3-1).

The flying wing is also of interest to the military in its quest for Stealth aircraft with "low observables." At least when viewed from the front and sides, the flying wing has a small radar cross-section (RCS), the characteristic that determines

Fig. 3-1. Because of their reduced drag and bending loads, the flying wings could reappear in the very large air freighters of the 21st century. A Boeing 747 is shown for comparison. (Courtesy Lockheed Georgia)

28

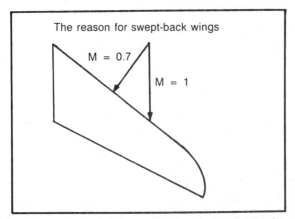

The reason for swept-back wings

M = 0.7

M = 1

Fig. 3-2. When a swept wing is flying at supersonic speeds, it only "sees" that portion of the velocity that is perpendicular to the leading edge of the wing. In the example shown here, while the wing has a forward speed of Mach 1, because the wing is swept back 45°, the wing "thinks" it is only flying at Mach 0.7.

how difficult it is for enemies to detect the aircraft on their radar screens. This is a result of the flying wing's flat profile, its lack of large vertical surfaces that reflect radar signals. Also, the engines, which give off detectable heat (infrared radiation) and can be destroyed by heat-seeking missiles, can be buried deep in the wings.

The Swept-Back and Swept-Forward Wings

As the speed of the air over a wing increases to transonic and supersonic speeds, there is a dramatic increase in drag—to the point that the aircraft can no longer accelerate. To overcome this, wings have been swept back to ever increasing angles, as

seen on fast-flying aircraft like the F-15, F-16, and *Concorde* (FIG. 3-2).

There are also advantages to be gained by sweeping the wings forward, even though such a design might appear weird at first glance. Like so many other ideas, forward-swept wings are not a brand-new idea. The Germans built the Ju-287 bomber with a forward-swept wing during World War II, and the German-designed HFB Hansa 320 business jet first flew with a forward-swept wing in 1964. The main motivation for these designs was the fact that by using forward-swept wings their attachment point could be moved farther aft. This permitted a larger bomb bay near the center of gravity, in the case of the Ju-287, and a longer cabin unimpeded by the wing spar for the HFB business jet. The designers of the Ju-287 also realized that the forward-swept wing was a means of avoiding the classic problem of tip-stall found on rearward-swept wings. Tip-stall results in reduced lift and could even lead to pitching up or loss of lateral control as a stall condition is approached (FIG. 3-3).

The problem inherent in forward-swept wings that has prevented their widespread use until now is the fact that they become severely loaded at high speeds—the exact conditions where wing sweep is needed. A conventional wing *washes out* toward the tip, that is, the angle of incidence (the angle between the wing chord and the line of thrust) decreases toward the wing tip as it bends under lift loads. With a forward-swept wing just the opposite happens. The wing *washes in,* adding to the load at the tip and causing the wing to bend even more.

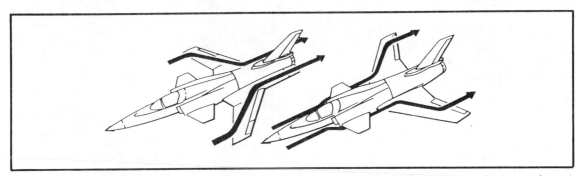

Fig. 3-3. With the forward-swept wing, the airflow tends to flow inward towards the wing root, while on the rearward-swept wing just the opposite occurs. This allows the former to remain unstalled up to a higher angle of attack. Additionally, the stall tends to occur nearer to the wing root, and thus is easier to control. (Courtesy Grumman Corporation)

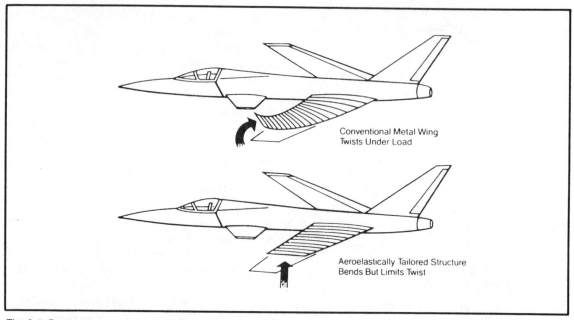

Fig. 3-4. Because composite materials are stiff in only one direction, the forward-swept wing can be tailored to bend in a specific direction under aerodynamic loads, such as those that cause divergence. By crisscrossing the composite materials during construction of the wing, it can be designed to bend but resist twisting under the high loads of maneuvering. (Courtesy Grumman Corporation)

In fact, at high speeds the loads can become so great that the results can be catastrophic. This phenomenon, called torsional or structural divergence, can be avoided by simply beefing-up the wing so it is able to withstand the large bending loads. But this results in an excessively heavy airplane if a conventional metal structure is used.

Fortunately, lightweight composite materials have come to the rescue of the forward-swept wing, so the level of interest in the design is currently high. Aeroelastically-tailored composites, as they are called, can be manufactured so that their fibers provide the greatest strength in the direction needed to resist the torsional divergence load, and they can do this without a weight penalty (FIG. 3-4).

What are the other advantages of the swept-forward wing that makes it so attractive today? The swept-forward wing results in higher lift coefficients than its swept-back counterpart. While this factor might not be greatly appreciated during normal cruise, it would be during high-speed conditions such as a high-performance fighter would experience (FIG. 3-5). Also, forward-swept wings do not

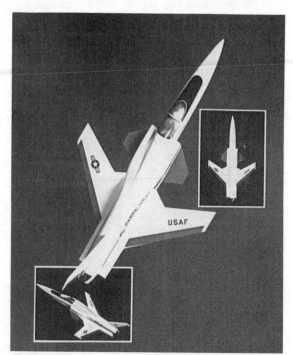

Fig. 3-5. While the X-29 isn't the first aircraft to use a forward-swept wing, it is the best performing. (Grumman Corporation)

30

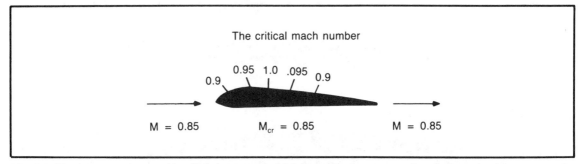

The critical mach number

0.9   0.95 1.0 .095 0.9

M = 0.85   M$_{cr}$ = 0.85   M = 0.85

Fig. 3-6. The reason a wing provides lift is because the airflow across the upper surface is faster (and the pressure is lower) than the flow across the lower surface. Thus, even when a wing flies at subsonic speed, it is possible that the upper airflow will reach Mach 1 or even higher velocities. The flight Mach number at which the airflow is accelerated to exactly Mach 1 somewhere on the airfoil is called the critical Mach number. In this example, the aircraft is only at Mach 0.85 when the airflow reaches Mach 1.

have to be swept as severely to handle the drag-rise problem for the same Mach number. Because the leading edge has less sweep, a higher lift-to-drag ratio can be achieved.

The forward-swept wing can be shorter and still provide the same lift surface, shock sweep angle, and effective wingspan, resulting in a lighter wing. Conversely, by keeping the strength to resist bending loads and the structural weight the same, the wing's aspect ratio can be reduced, leading to less drag—always an important gain.

Supercritical Wing

Even though an aircraft might not be flying at supersonic speeds, it is possible that the airflow over the aircraft, especially over the wings, can reach the point where it reaches supersonic speeds and there is a sudden and dramatic increase in drag. The airspeed at which this occurs is called the critical Mach number (FIGS. 3-6 AND 3-7). On a typical wing, the location where the airflow speed exceeds Mach 1 is usually near the wing's midpoint, or in aerodynamic terms, at about the 40-percent chord location. Here the typical wing has its greatest curvature and the air is moving at its fastest velocity. The critical Mach number is higher for thin wings than for thick ones.

In the mid-1960s, Dr. Richard Whitcomb of NASA began his research on the supercritical wing. The supercritical wing has a special design that delays formation of a shock wave until a higher critical speed. The resultant drag rise is also delayed.

Surprisingly, the supercritical wing is considerably thicker for the same lift-to-drag ratio. Thus, the designer can either keep the same thickness and reduce the drag, or maintain the same drag and have a thicker wing (FIG. 3-8). Thick wings have many good points. They provide more lift and do not stall as abruptly. Thick wings also can be made stronger and lighter, and there is more room in the wing for fuel tanks and other equipment. Inciden-

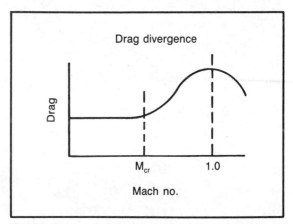

Fig. 3-7. At low subsonic speeds, the drag produced by an airfoil is essentially constant. As the freestream velocity approaches the critical Mach number there is a dramatic increase in drag. Aerodynamicists call this drag divergence, and the critical Mach number is sometimes called the divergence Mach number. The drag continues to rise rapidly till about Mach 1. In the early days of flight, some experts thought drag would increase infinitely at Mach 1, and thus the idea of the sonic barrier was in vogue. However, Chuck Yeager and his X-1 showed that the sonic barrier could be penetrated and that after Mach 1, drag starts to decrease again.

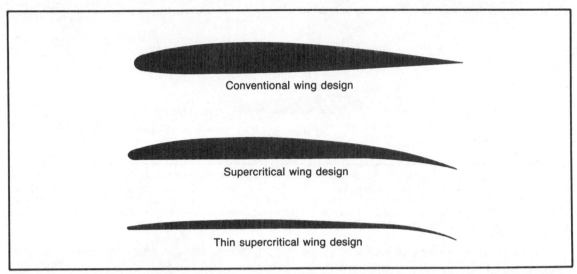

Conventional wing design

Supercritical wing design

Thin supercritical wing design

Fig. 3-8. The supercritical wing delays and reduces the strength of the shock waves on the upper surface at transonic speeds. The Grumman X-29 will be the first aircraft to fly with the thin supercritical wing. (Courtesy Grumman Corporation)

Fig. 3-9. The Gulfstream IV business jet is one of many new aircraft designs that use winglets. (Courtesy Gulfstream Aero space)

tally, supercritical wings not only are of use on high-speed aircraft, but also are of benefit to commercial and general-aviation aircraft, which fly much slower.

Winglets

Among the other important contributions made by NASA's Dr. Whitcomb are the winglets (first used on the *Learjet*) that are already seen on some of the latest aircraft and will be an important feature on aircraft of the future (FIG. 3-9).

An airfoil produces lift because of a difference in pressure on the upper and lower surfaces. At the tips of the wings this pressure differential causes air to flow from the lower to the upper surface. This results in a swirling flow of air that trails behind the aircraft, a phenomenon known as wingtip vortices. The more lift a wing is producing, the greater is the strength of the vortices. Not only does the wingtip-vortex effect increase drag and decrease the lift produced by a wing, it can cause havoc around airports. The vortices shed by a heavy aircraft like a Boeing 747 can trail the aircraft for miles before they finally are dissipated. Other aircraft flying into the vortices can be severely buffeted. Flying light aircraft too close to an aircraft shedding vortices can be extremely dangerous.

Dr. Whitcomb came up with the winglet, a remarkably simple solution to eliminate the wingtip vortices, or at least to reduce their strength substantially. A winglet added at a precisely determined angle with respect to the main wing not only overcomes the vortex problem, but improves the efficiency of the wing, leading to reduced fuel consumption. The wingtip tanks found on many military fighters provide a similar effect, although not an optimum one, as in the case of a well designed winglet.

Fig. 3-10. Tests of wingtip wind turbines installed on a Piper PA-28 showed that over twenty percent of the energy required to overcome drag induced by wingtip vortices could be recovered.

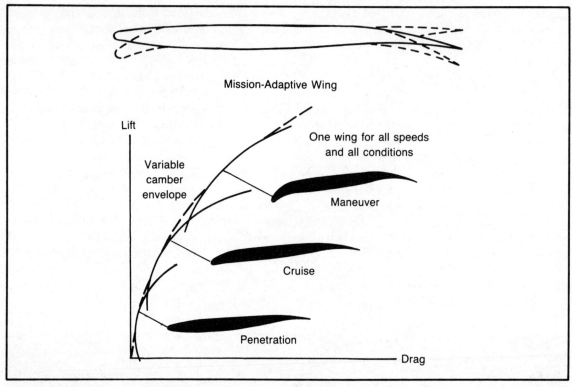

Fig. 3-11. The mission-adaptive wing (MAW) is designed to provide optimum performance under varying flight conditions. This graph shows how well an MAW compares with an ideal variable-camber-envelope airfoil. The MAW automatically reconfigures during flight. (Courtesy Boeing Aircraft)

Wingtip Vortex Turbines

This new idea takes the principles of the winglets one step farther. In place of the winglets, wind turbines are added at the end of each wing. Besides reducing the vortex strength and drag, these turbines extract energy from the swirling air (FIG. 3-10). The turbines can be connected to generators that produce electricity to be used aboard the aircraft. Engineers predict that up to 400 horsepower could be generated if a similar system is installed on a Boeing 747.

Mission-Adaptive Wings

A wing design is a compromise. For example, if a designer wants a wing for an aircraft that will cruise at supersonic speeds, he must also design the wing to fly at subsonic speeds as well as for take-off and landings. Thus, the optimum cruise con-figuration is compromised to gain the other necessary characteristics. Granted, devices such as ailerons, flaps, spoilers, and slats can partially compensate for deficiencies, but these still do not give the optimum performance of a wing designed for a particular flight regime.

The answer is a mission-adaptive wing that maintains its peak aerodynamic efficiency under almost all flight conditions (FIG. 3-11). This is done by changing the shape of the wing (like a bird does). Using flexible composite materials and an on-board computer for assistance, actuators buried below the surface of the wing can vary the surface contour as demanded by pilot control and flight conditions. Unlike flaps, spoilers, slats, and ailerons, which are appendages to the wing, the mission-adaptive wing is one piece (FIG. 3-12).

Fig. 3-12. Opposite: A prototype of the MAW is being flight tested on the AFTI F-111. (Courtesy Boeing Aircraft)

34

The Oblique Wing

As mentioned previously, swept-back wings are needed for high-speed supersonic flight. However, the swept wing does not provide enough lift to allow sufficiently slow approach and landing speeds. One way to have both good low- and high-speed flight characteristics in the same aircraft is to use a variable-geometry wing. For example, the main wings on the Air Force's F-111 are extended for takeoffs, landings, and low-speed flight, but they are swept back for flight at supersonic speeds. While this has been quite a satisfactory solution, the bearings and mechanical parts for pivoting the wing must be very substantial, and thus quite heavy, in order to handle the bending loads produced by the wings.

A few years back, prominent NASA aerodynamicist Dr. Bob Jones came up with a solution to the problem. (Incidentally, Dr. Jones was the instigator of swept-back wings in the 1940s.) The solution was the scissor, or oblique, wing. The oblique wing is a slender wing that can be pivoted about its center point. For takeoffs, landings, and low-speed flight, the wing would be positioned at right angles to the fuselage. For flight at supersonic speeds, it would be pivoted up to 60 degrees (FIGS. 3-13 AND 3-14). While this scissor-like appearance may look odd—one wing is pointed forward and the other one is pointed aft—it has very little effect on the aircraft's flight. Like a forward-swept wing, the wing itself does not care whether the sweep is forward or rearward.

Because the oblique wing is one continuous piece, it absorbs most of the bending loads so that pivot bearings need not be as massive as with a conventional variable-geometry arrangement. Because the wing can be made very slender, it has a high aspect ratio, just what is needed for efficient operation at low speeds, low power requirements, and low fuel consumption. Lower power requirements also lead to less noise and pollution.

The Joined Wing

Another concept that looks somewhat weird, but works very well, is the joined wing (PLATE 13). Like other concepts, joined wings are almost as old as the airplane itself. Only recently, however, has there been a serious interest in the concept within the aerospace community. The primary force behind this renewed interest is Dr. Julian Wolkovitch, who holds most of the key patents on this unique design. The joined-wing aircraft has its main and tail wings joined near their tips so that, when viewed from either the top or front, the wings form a diamond. To do this, the main wing is swept rearward and the tail wing is swept forward. The wing

Fig. 3-13. The oblique wing's single span would be rotated in flight to allow the aircraft to operate efficiently both at high and low speeds. (Courtesy NASA)

Fig. 3-14. Here is an artist's concept of the oblique wing adapted to an F-8 fuselage for flight testing. (Courtesy NASA)

are joined at the tips, or at a point inboard of the front wingtips.

The advantages of the joined wing over a conventional wing include lighter weight, greater stiffness, lower drag, and higher lift, plus improved stability and control. The joined wing can also provide unique maneuvering capability (FIG. 3-15). The lighter weight comes from the way in which the wings can be constructed. For a conventional wing, a box-type structure is used to resist the bending loads that come primarily from the lift. A large amount of material is needed on the top and bottom of the box structure, and this means lots of weight. With a joined wing, the lift load is broken into two components, one acting along the plane of the joined wing and another, much larger, component acting perpendicular to the plane formed by the wings. Because of the orientation of this perpendicular component of lift, the bulk of the wing material can be located near the leading and trailing edges. Because resistance to bending is dependent upon both the amount of material and the beam depth, the large effective beam depth makes up for a lot of material, thus substantially reducing weight. The material in the leading and trailing edges is at just the right location to maintain leading edge contours for good aerodynamics and, at the trailing edge, to handle the loads produced by control surfaces and flaps.

Even though joined wings are thinner, they are stiffer, because torsional loads on one set of wings are resisted by the flexure of the other set. In wind tunnel tests, joined wings have been found to have less induced drag than conventional wings, as well as maximum lift coefficients. Thinner wings can be used, and because there is less wetted area (area in contact with the air), parasitic drag is reduced.

By putting control surfaces on both sets of wings, some interesting maneuvering is possible. By deflecting the front and rear surfaces in opposite directions large pitching moments result. Deflecting all the surfaces down makes them act as flaps, providing high, direct, lift control. To obtain powerful roll control, the surfaces can be used as ailerons. If the control surfaces on the front and rear wings are deflected to give equal, but opposite rolling moments, direct side-force control is obtained, and you have the unique ability to move sideways.

Canards

While canards are as old are as the airplane itself, it has only been recently that they have come into their own. They will be a design feature of many aircraft of the future, from fighters to ultralights. Some experts even consider the canard the most revolutionary change in basic aircraft design (FIG. 3-16).

Fig. 3-15. Opposite: The joined-wing concept results in not only a lighter aircraft, but also a more maneuverable one. (Courtesy Julian Wolkovitch)

In order to prevent an aircraft from pitching in an oscillating manner, its aerodynamic center must be fairly well separated from the center of gravity. For stability, the center of gravity is located forward of the aerodynamic center. In the past, most aircraft used horizontal stabilizers to counteract the nose-down attitude attributed to the center of gravity's forward location. But canards can also perform the function while also producing positive lift, allowing the main wings to be smaller and lighter. By contrast, the typical horizontal tail produces negative lift, so the main wings must be larger to compensate for the loss of lift. In addition, canards are never in the downwash of the wings, so unlike a horizontal tail, they are effective at high angles of attack. This last characteristic is important in high-performance aircraft, which will operate at very high angles of attack to achieve supermaneuverability.

Canards are now practical because aeronautical engineers now know how to prevent the in-

Fig. 3-16. Burt Rutan pioneered both the canard and composite construction. Here they are used in their simplest form, a glider. (Rutan Aircraft Factory)

stability problems experienced in the past. Most of the success in using canards can be traced to the work of aeronautical genius Burt Rutan.

Laminar Flow Control

Close to the surface of every wing in flight is a very thin sheet of air called the *boundary layer*. At low speeds, this boundary layer follows the contours of the airfoil and is very smooth. Indeed, under these conditions the flow is called *laminar* because the fluid particles are moving in well-ordered "layers." As the airspeed increases, the flow transitions to turbulent, where there is much mixing of particles between layers. Turbulent flow results in much greater surface friction and drag. The idea behind laminar flow control is to maintain laminar flow over the entire surface of the wing at high speeds, and thus reduce drag.

One method of obtaining laminar flow control is to suck off a portion of the boundary through holes or slots in the surface of the airfoil, or to construct the actual airfoil surface of a porous material (FIGS. 3-17 AND 3-18). Pumps below the airfoil surface are needed for the suction, and ducting is required to vent the air from the airfoil surface to the atmosphere outside.

While the benefits of laminar flow (or boundary-layer control, as it is sometimes called) have been known for years, and even demonstrated in flight tests, the concept has not actually been put into application. For example, it offers over a 25-percent potential reduction in fuel consumption when used in subsonic commercial airliners. However, the pumps and ducting become quite complex and represent a sizable weight penalty. Also, means have not yet been perfected to prevent dirt and insects from clogging, eroding, and corroding the very small suction holes and slots and the pumping and ducting systems. This currently presents an unacceptable maintenance problem, especially for the commercial airline operators.

A much simpler approach to maintaining laminar flow, with all its attendant advantages, is called natural laminar flow (NLF). By properly shaping the wing and making its surface extremely smooth, the transition from laminar to turbulent flow can be delayed so that laminar flow is retained over most of the wing. High technology has made NLF possible. The very accurate wing contour is designed by computer; the very smooth surface is a result of composite materials. Unfortunately, surface roughening by bugs and ice can still present a problem.

Circulation Control

Somewhat akin to the idea of a boundary-layer control is the idea of circulation control. Here, however, air is blown out through one or more slots in a wing (rather than being sucked into the wing) to increase the circulation of the free-stream air around the airfoil and thus substantially increase the lift.

Typically, a source of compressed air, usually an engine-driven pump or bleed air from the turbine, supplies pressurized air to a plenum chamber in the wing. The air then flows through a slot located near the trailing edge of the wing. (Some designs also call for slots in the leading edge.) This escaping air causes the air flowing over the top of the wing to accelerate. By accelerating the air, lift is increased. Drag, however, is decreased.

X-Wing

The X-wing carries the concept of the oblique or scissor wing one step farther. It produces an air-

WHAT IS LAMINAR FLOW CONTROL ?

- NORMAL SURFACE LAYER

    THICK AND TURBULENT WITH HIGH DRAG

- SUCTION - STABILIZED SURFACE LAYER

    THIN AND LAMINAR WITH LOW DRAG

- BENEFIT: MINIMUM 20% FUEL SAVING OVER FUTURE TURBULENT TRANSPORTS

Fig. 3-17. This is how laminar flow is maintained through suction of the boundary layer. (Courtesy NASA)

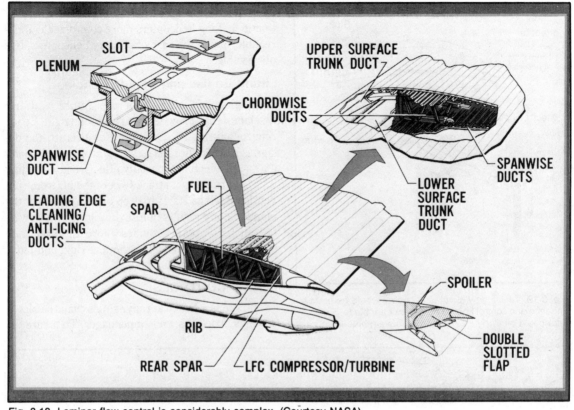

Fig. 3-18. Laminar flow control is considerably complex. (Courtesy NASA)

ing characteristics of a helicopter with the performance of a high-performance aircraft.

The X-wing operates just like a helicopter, with the X-wing serving as rotor blades during low-speed flight. Once the "rotors" accelerate the aircraft to around 200 knots (about the top speed for a conventional helicopter), the wing is stopped and locked into place. At high speeds, the blades function just like conventional wings.

Circulation control, mentioned previously, would probably be an integral part of the X-wing aircraft. To prevent a helicopter from rolling over, the amount of lift produced by the rotor blades changes constantly as the rotor rotates. Also, the lift of the blades is changed as the helicopter climbs, descends, turns, hovers, or increases or decreases its forward speed. In a conventional helicopter, the change in lift is accomplished by changing the pitch

(angle of attack) of the blades. This requires a complex arrangement of mechanisms that includes a swash plate, pitch horns, control rods, levers, and other mechanical paraphernalia.

With a circulation-control rotor design, changes in lift would be accomplished simply by regulating the amount of air blown through the slots (FIGS. 3-19 AND 3-20). The rotor, which would be rigidly attached to the mast, would still rotate mechanically through a transmission connected to the engine. A set of valves would be used to control the amount of compressed air passing through the plenum in the wings and out the slots. The valves would be controlled by the pilot as part of the flight control system.

Not only does the circulation-control rotor offer the potential for a simpler, cheaper, and more easily maintained rotor control system, it operates

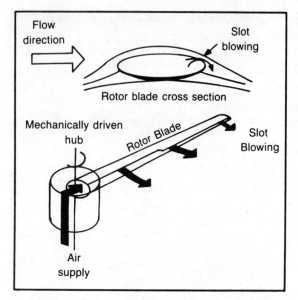

Fig. 3-19. This is how circulation control would be used to enhance and control lift on a helicopter rotor blade. The concept could similarly be used on a conventional wing.

more quietly and with less vibration. This is important in making helicopters more comfortable, more reliable, and in the case of military helicopters, less observable.

Lifting Bodies and Blended Bodies

High-speed aircraft of the future will use fuselages that provide lift, resembling the Space Shuttle's lifting-body design. For aircraft, the design is commonly referred to as a ''blended'' body (FIG. 3-21), which is especially effective in providing lift at high angles of attack (where the lift from conventional wings starts to drop off). In addition, the blended body results in less drag (due to less wetted surface area), provides more internal fuel-storage capacity, and allows a more rigid and lighter-weight structure.

FLIGHT CONTROLS

There is more to aerodynamics than the shape of wings, fuselages, and empennages. There are the

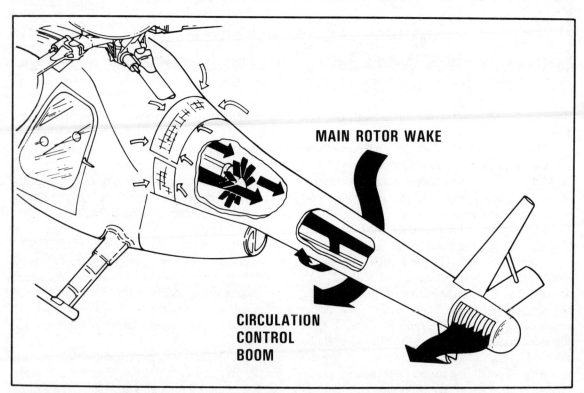

Fig. 3-20. Circulation control can eliminate the tail rotor on a helicopter by supplying the necessary side (yaw) forces. A special nozzle at the tip of the tail helps at low speeds. (Courtesy Hughes Helicopters)

Fig. 3-21. A wind-tunnel model of the F-16 showing its blended-body design. (Courtesy U.S. Air Force)

various control surfaces, such as elevators, rudders, flaps, and so forth. How these devices are controlled has a significant effect on the aircraft's performance characteristics.

Flight controls now on the drawing board, being tested in the laboratory, and being flown on research aircraft will allow aircraft to do some amazing things and, in the process, will result in better fuel economy, longer aircraft life, less maintenance, safer flying, and even a better ride in turbulent air.

Active Flight Controls

In a conventional aircraft, the pilot uses his stick (or control yoke) and his pedals to turn, climb, or descend. Active controls are automatic controls that operate independently of the pilot. A computer receives input commands from sensors located at appropriate locations on the airplane, makes its decision, and transmits this decision in the form of electronic commands to the control surfaces. The pilot still commands the aircraft, but the active controls respond to the external forces that happen so rapidly that the pilot cannot take action fast enough.

Here is an example of how active controls might operate on a commercial transport:

Turbulence is something airline pilots like to avoid, not only because passengers dislike it, but also because it puts a tremendous strain on the airframe. Circumstances such as bad weather and air traffic, however, might require airliners to fly through the worst turbulence.

Suppose a turbulence sensor was mounted on a boom extending out in front of the airliner. The sensor would feel the turbulence ahead of the airplane and also determine its direction and strength. This information would be sent to the control system, where it would be translated into commands for corrective control action. All of this would happen in a fraction of a second—much faster than a human could sense the turbulence and react. Not only would such a system result in a smoother ride, it would greatly reduce the bouncing and pounding an airplane takes when flying in turbulence. The airframe would last longer and could even be much lighter, leading to reduced cost.

The military is interested in turbulence alleviation for its low-flying bombers. To avoid radar detection, bombers fly "on-the-deck" at high speeds with severe turbulence. Turbulence hammers the bomber's airframe and bounces the crew around so much that they cannot focus their eyes on their instruments or the world outside.

Active controls could also be used to change the lift distribution across the span of the wing. The lift produced near the tips could be reduced, and the lift produced near the roots (where the wing joins the fuselage) could be increased. This would result in reduced bending loads, and wings could be made lighter.

Because wings are quite flexible, at high speeds and when maneuvered violently they can vibrate rapidly, causing what is commonly called "flutter." Wing flutter can become so severe that the wings can be torn off the fuselage. The normal approach to solving flutter problems is to make the wing stiffer, and usually heavier. An active-control system could sense the onset of flutter and automatically adjust auxiliary control surfaces on the wing to increase the stiffness "aerodynamically," with a much smaller weight penalty.

Finally, an aircraft is highly stressed during maneuvers. For example, unlike straight-and-level flight (where loads might be large but are symmetrical), in a sharp turn the wing can be bent or twisted in a non-uniform manner. The wing must be over-designed to handle this non-symmetrical loading. By using a form of active control that automatically deflects the trailing edge of the flaps, the lift distribution can be tailored to reduce wing bending.

Aeroelastically Tailored Wings

As mentioned earlier, composite material woven into wings has made the high-speed forward-swept-wing aircraft feasible. This material also offers a form of "active" control that does not involve the complexity of sensors or computers.

Composite wings can take advantage of the unidirectional stiffness of their materials. Wings made of composites consist of layers, or plies, of material woven on top of one another. By carefully designing the way the plies are woven (i.e., the direction in which the strongest fibers run), the wing can be made to bend so as to give the best

lift and drag characteristics for a given set of flight conditions.

Relaxed Static Stability

The conventional aircraft has been designed to automatically return to straight-and-level flight after being disturbed by a gust or a pilot command. This is called positive static stability and is the result of the proper design and location of the horizontal and vertical tails as well as wing dihedral.

Although positive static stability might be desirable in a "forgiving" light airplane or even a commercial airliner, it is definitely a hindrance to superior maneuverability in a high-performance fighter. Typically, fighters are designed with little or no static stability.

While providing good maneuvering characteristics, relaxed static stability requires the pilot to fly the aircraft, hands-on, all the time. To reduce pilot workload, and in some cases even make the aircraft possible to fly in the first place, a stability augmentation system is needed to compensate for the lack of static stability; this system would be a form of active control.

Fly-by-Wire Control System

In the early days of aviation, flight control surfaces were connected with the pilot's controls through a maze of cables, bell cranks, pulleys, and a variety of other mechanical components. In later years, these mechanical systems were augmented by hydraulic control systems that enhanced the pilots' control forces in high-performance military aircraft and commercial transports. While giving much more responsive control, these systems were very complex and added significantly to the weight of the aircraft.

With the recent revolution of *fly-by-wire*, the mechanical connections between a pilot's controls and the control-surface actuators are replaced by wires that carry electrical signals. In addition to the wires, there are various electromechanical devices that convert stick and rudder-pedal motions into electrical voltages. These voltages are measured, and their values are fed into a digital computer. The computer is programmed with a set of control laws that make the aircraft "flyable." The computer output, again in the form of electrical signals, is fed by wire to the actuators which, in turn, move the control surfaces.

Fly-by-wire was first used on early manned spacecraft like the *Mercury, Gemini,* and *Apollo*; much more sophisticated systems were installed on the Space Shuttle. Military fighters like the General Dynamics F-16 and Northrop F/A-18 already use fly-by-wire control systems. Fly-by-wire is also found on the *Concorde* and Airbus Industrie A320 commercial airliners.

Besides reducing weight, fly-by-wire provides more responsive control and makes multiple, redundant, flight-control systems easier to build. Also, it is possible to change the flight characteristics of an aircraft simply by reprogramming the control laws in the computer. In the future, it might be possible to change an interceptor to a ground-attack fighter or a photo-reconnaissance aircraft by simply rewriting computer software and changing weapons and mission equipment. The Swedes are already using this idea in their new Saab JAS-39 *Gripen* multirole combat fighter.

Another interesting example of the use of fly-by-wire technology is the self-repairing flight-control system being developed by the Air Force. In combat, an aircraft's primary control surfaces could suffer battle damage or even be completely blown away. By instantaneously reconfiguring the flight-control system, primarily by using alternate flight-control laws, the surviving control surfaces (like rudders, flaperons, ailerons or stabilizers) could be used in combination to perform the functions of the lost surface. This would not only keep the aircraft from crashing, but also allow the aircraft to fly safely home and, in many cases, even complete its mission.

Fly-by-Light Control System

The *fly-by-light* concept replaces wires with optical fibers. Signals are transmitted along the optical fibers at the speed of light using light from a laser. Because a single optical fiber the thickness of a human hair can carry a tremendous amount of information, heavy wiring can be replaced by featherweight optical-fiber cables. The fiber optics are also impervious to electromagnetic radiation, an important consideration for military aircraft that must operate in an environment of electronic countermeasure and even in the fallout from nuclear weapons. Fly-by-light control systems can be built without electromagnetic shielding (which adds to total aircraft weight).

AERODYNAMICS AND SURVIVABILITY

A military aircraft's survivability is enhanced by its ability to escape detection by the enemy. One of the biggest challenges facing military aircraft designers today and in the future is the need for aircraft with "low observables," that is, aircraft that are "invisible" to sophisticated enemy sensors (FIG. 3-22). These sensors can detect an aircraft by its radar, infrared, acoustic, and visible signatures. Indeed, if you name a characteristic of an airplane, with today's and tomorrow's state of electronic technology, a sensor can be developed to discriminate the signature and use it to detect and destroy the plane.

The other part of the survivability equation is that, if detected, the pilot must be able to survive enemy interceptors, guns, and missiles. A key way to accomplish this is by maneuvering to avoid them. Aerodynamics play the significant role here, and today there is a great deal of research being done to provide aircraft, primarily fighters, with super-maneuverability.

Stealth

The story of low observables could fill books, except that most of it is highly classified, as it should be. A single leak of a critical detail could negate years of research, not to mention the U.S.'s advantage over its enemies. Because of this, we will explain only a few of the aerodynamic techniques for reducing observables—ones based on basic physical and engineering principles—to give a flavor of the complexity of the problem facing the aerodynamicist and aeronautical engineer.

Magazines and newspapers have been filled with artists' ideas of what Stealth fighters and bombers of the future might look like. And while there

Fig. 3-22. Opposite: The Lockheed SR-71 is a good example of how the need for low observables affects the complete design of an aircraft. The blended body, chines, and inward-canted tail fins all help to foil enemy radars. (Courtesy Lockheed-California Company)

are almost as many ideas as there are artists, most share some common aerodynamic features.

For starters, most are flying wings. This shape has the lowest radar cross section (RCS), at least when viewed head-on. The flying wing's low RCS was known when Northrop designed the flying-wing bombers during World War II, partially to counter the growing threat from German radars. The British-built *Vulcan* bomber with its V-shaped wing platform, has a low RCS, but it also has poor range, demonstrating the aerodynamic penalty to be paid for stealth capabilities.

The flying wing has a very low visible signature when viewed from the front, rear, or side, but not from above or below. You will not find any corners on Stealth aircraft, especially corners where surfaces mate at 90-degree angles. In just about every design, the tail surfaces are mounted obliquely to the fuselage—if there is a tail at all. Sharp corners are great radar reflectors and are often placed purposely on small objects to increase their radar reflections. There are also no gaps, cracks, or openings on the fuselage; these also are great RCS enhancers. Completely vertical tail fins and slab-sided fuselages are forbidden because of the way they reflect radar energy. Finally, weapons are carried internally, rather than hung on the wings and fuselage where they would present a very "dirty" radar image. The end result is a blended body that approaches the concept of a lifting body with very smooth contours and surfaces.

Engines give stealth designers some real headaches. Engines and their exhaust give off tremendous infrared signatures. In many stealth designs the engines are buried in the upper portion of the fuselage where they cannot be seen very well from below by infrared (IR) sensors. The inlets take a lot of very careful designing to reduce their RCS. While the stealth characteristics are enhanced by these propulsion system designs, in many cases engine performance is degraded.

Speaking of IR signatures, the Stealth aircraft will probably not be a very-high-speed aircraft, at least when attempting to penetrate enemy defenses. High speeds, especially supersonic speeds, lead to heating of the skin to high temperatures, resulting in very high infrared signatures. A subsonic cruise speed of about Mach 0.8 would be optimum for these aircraft.

As you can see, using aerodynamics to reduce observables results in many compromises.

Supermaneuverability

Supermaneuverability is defined as the capability of a fighter to perform maneuvers at angles of attack beyond the point of stall, as well as controlled side-slip maneuvers. The need for supermaneuverability has been brought about by increased capabilities of Soviet weapons systems (or at least by intelligence agency estimates of future Soviet capabilities).

One of the first operational aircraft to use a form of supermaneuverability was the AV-8 *Harrier* V/STOL fighter with its vectored-thrust engines. Normally, the exhaust of the engine points downward for vertical flight and rearward for horizontal flight. However, by pointing the nozzles a bit forward, the *Harrier* can perform some maneuvers that are guaranteed to confuse (and hopefully defeat) the enemy. Using vectoring-in-forward-flight (VIFF), the *Harrier* can decelerate more rapidly than any other aircraft. In a dogfight with the enemy on its tail, the *Harrier* can slow down so suddenly that, to the adversary, it appears to have stopped in midair. The hunter would then be the hunted. This is just one of a multitude of interesting tactics available with VIFF.

A few years ago, the Air Force modified an F-16 into the Controlled Configuration Vehicle, the CCV-16. The main changes were the eight-square-foot ventral canards mounted on each side of the engine inlet duct (FIG. 3-23). There were also changes to the fuel tank arrangement (to move the aircraft's center of gravity farther back) and to the flight-control system. These changes radically changed the aircraft's flying characteristics. For example, the aircraft's nose could be pointed in any

Fig. 3-23. Opposite: Ventral canards on a CCV-modified F-16 allowed it to perform some radical flight maneuvers. (Courtesy General Dynamics)

direction without changing the direction of flight. It could move sideways without banking or rolling. It could climb, descend, or move sideways without changing the direction of the nose. Just think of the possibilities this capability would give the fighter pilot.

Today, basic research is being done on wing aerodynamics at angles of attack beyond the point of stall. While wing stall has always been something designers and pilots have religiously tried to avoid, in the future, aircraft may fly in the post-stall regime to achieve supermaneuverability.

For example, wind tunnel research has shown that by rapidly pitching an airfoil past the stall angle of attack, it is possible to achieve several times the lift compared to the same wing flown in normal flight. The results of the research, commonly categorized under the generic title "unsteady aerodynamics," offers some interesting possibilities for the future. Scientists are even studying in great detail how Mother Nature's creatures, such as the dragonfly, perform their unique flight maneuvers, hoping someday to adapt what they learn to man-made aircraft.

Future high-performance fighters will be able to do things only dreamt of by today's hottest fighter pilots.

AERODYNAMICS RESEARCH AND DEVELOPMENT

As the saying goes, "the proof is in the pudding." In the development of new aerodynamic concepts, the proof comes during the idea's flight test. Building manned experimental aircraft for flight testing is an expensive proposition, so, many techniques have been developed to try out new ideas relatively inexpensively, saving final proof testing to the very end.

Wind Tunnels

The Wright brothers were using wind tunnels to do aerodynamic research before their historic first flight at Kitty Hawk. Through the years, wind tunnels have grown in sophistication to keep up with the need to fly faster and higher. This growth will continue into the future with new capabilities derived from advances in electronics, materials, and propulsion technologies.

The *Reynolds number* is a key parameter in describing the capabilities of a wind tunnel. The idea is to have the Reynolds number in the test as close as possible to the Reynolds number of the actual aircraft.* As flight speeds and aircraft size increase, this becomes much more difficult. For example, a giant air freighter might have a Reynolds number of around 125,000,000. Up until recently, the best of NASA's wind tunnels could only simulate Reynolds numbers of about 15,000,000.

A major step forward was taken in the early 1980s with the opening of the National Transonic Facility, located at the NASA Langley Research Facility in Virginia. The development of aircraft that will fly at hypersonic speeds (Mach 5 to Mach 25) will place even greater demand on wind tunnels. Currently there is a substantial effort in the United States to upgrade tunnel capabilities to meet these needs (FIG. 3-24).

In addition to the high-technology tunnels themselves, great strides are being made in the methods used to take data and gain information during tests. Because wind-tunnel testing is very expensive, it is important that data acquisition be done very efficiently. High-speed computers are a major factor here, as is the laser.

The laser velocimeter has become a very important tool in obtaining data during wind-tunnel

---

*The Reynolds number is defined by:

$$\text{REYNOLDS NUMBER} = \frac{\text{VELOCITY} \times \text{CHARACTERISTIC DIMENSION}}{\text{FLUID VISCOSITY}}$$

The velocity is the freestream speed of the air flowing through the wind tunnel, or the airspeed of the actual airplane. The characteristic dimension could be the chord length of an airfoil or the diameter of an engine inlet duct. Because a scale model has a smaller characteristic dimension than an actual design, the tunnel speed must increase, the viscosity decrease, or both, if the same Reynolds number is to be attained.

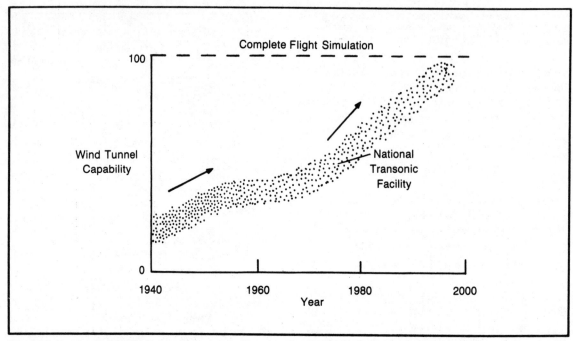

Fig. 3-24. Eventually, the full flight envelopes of many aircraft will be completely simulated in wind tunnels, eliminating most, but not all, need for expensive flight testing.

tests. Not only does it gather data at an extremely high rate, it does not disturb the airflow, unlike other flow measurement devices. Disturbed airflow sometimes causes erroneous results. The laser velocimeter and laser interferometer can also be used to look at the pattern of the airflow over the wind-tunnel model, replacing older techniques such as injecting smoke into the airstream or placing tufts of thread on the model. With the laser, aerodynamicists can get a moving picture of what is happening and a better understanding of the complete flow phenomenon.

Other important technological advances are being made to improve the accuracy of wind-tunnel simulations. For example, in wind-tunnel testing, the model must be supported in some manner. Today, this is usually done by a "sting" attached to the rear of the model. The sting supports the model and contains connections so information from sensors imbedded in the model can be transmitted to the instrumentation outside the tunnel. The sting, unfortunately, disturbs the airflow and adds extraneous readings that can lead to erroneous

results. Research is now being done on models suspended by magnetic levitation. Powerful superconducting magnets would not only suspend the model in midstream, "defying" the laws of gravity, but would also measure the aerodynamic forces on the models—the information the aerodynamicist needs. By varying the strength of the magnetic field, it might even be possible to accelerate and maneuver the model to simulate real flight conditions. The model could actually be flown in the wind tunnel.

The "Electronic" Wind Tunnel

The mathematics of aerodynamics are among the most complex of any physical science. Even a simple problem (e.g., solving the equations to describe non-turbulent airflow around an aircraft in straight-and-level flight) can take as many as 50 billion or more computer operations. When the flight is complicated by complex aircraft geometries, maneuvers, or turbulence, the number of operations jumps by orders of magnitude. Because of these seemingly insurmountable problems, aeronautical engineers and designers in the past re-

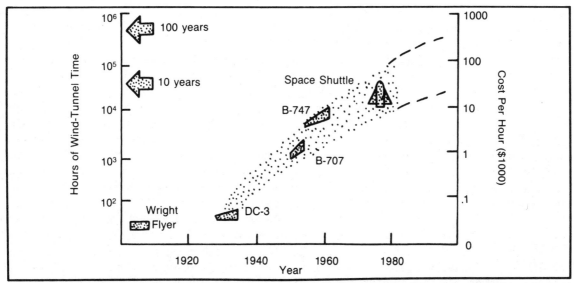

Fig. 3-25. From a few hours of tunnel time for the Wright flyer, total wind tunnel time for a new aircraft has increased to years. Cost per hour of tunnel time has also increased exponentially. Testing of the National Aerospace Plane will undoubtedly fall at the very top of this chart.

lied on the results of wind-tunnel tests and simple approximate solutions to mathematical equations.

Because wind-tunnel testing has become so expensive and even minor changes in a design can require a whole new set of tests, a great investment is being made in supercomputers that can solve the complex mathematics of aerodynamics (FIG. 3-25). Computer scientists often describe the speed of a supercomputer in terms of millions of floating-point operations per second, or Mflops.

Today, the hallmark of computer technology is the Cray-2 supercomputer, capable of storing 256 million words, a peak speed of 2000 Mflops, and a sustained speed of 250 Mflops (FIG. 3-26). By the end of this decade, capabilities should shoot up to a peak speed of 10,000 Mflops and a sustained speed of 1000 Mflops. By the 1990s, aerodynamicists should be able to work with computers with sustained speeds of 4000 Mflops and memories that can store in excess of a billion words.

The question is often asked as to whether the "electronic" wind tunnel will ever replace the real wind tunnel. The answer is a definite no. The two will always be around to complement one another. Experts say that computers able to design a complete aircraft, including its engines, will not arrive

Fig. 3-26. Supercomputers like this Cray-2 represent a major step toward simulating actual aircraft flight on a computer. This machine can perform 250 million continuous calculations per second. (Courtesy NASA)

51

for another 25 years. Such a computer would require capabilities at least 1000 times more powerful than the supercomputers now emerging (FIG. 3-27). And there will probably always be aircraft geometries and flight regimes that defy simulation by mathematical equations and computers. Also, no matter how accurate computer simulations become, wind-tunnel data will be required to verify the accuracy of the computer results. As the mathematical solutions are extrapolated to new regimes, test data is needed at various points along the way to insure that the extrapolations are pointed in the right direction.

Flight Tests

Aircraft designers must have confidence in a new aerodynamic concept before it is accepted and actually incorporated into production aircraft (FIG. 3-28). Normally, this confidence is gained after a triad of validation techniques. The triad consists of mathematical/computer simulations, wind-tunnel testing, and flight testing. Because flight testing is so expensive, it is usually saved until last. At that point, only one or two of the many designs tested have passed the computer and wind-tunnel tests and are actually installed on a test aircraft.

In the past few years a couple of rather revolutionary techniques have emerged to reduce the costs of flight testing. One of these is the subscale flying model, made of new composite materials and built with techniques borrowed from the light-aircraft and homebuilt-aircraft builder. The model is only a fraction of the size of the real airplane and can be built and tested for a fraction of the cost. Designs for such diverse aircraft as Beech's *Starship I*, the Air Force's Fairchild-developed T-46A trainer, and the oblique-wing airplane have already been built and tested in subscale form. (Interestingly, these were designed by Burt Rutan.) There are even plans to flight test a subscale hypersonic aircraft as a precursor to the National Aerospace Plane, albeit a much more sophisticated aircraft than existing subscale models.

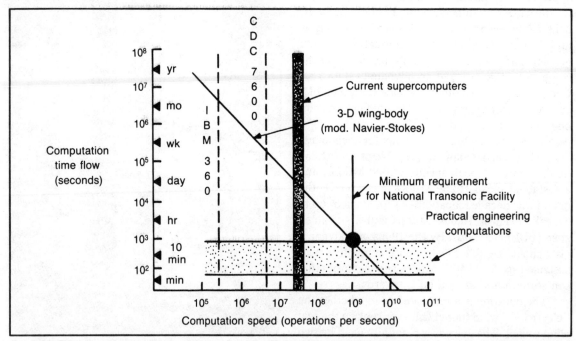

Fig. 3-27. This graphic shows how technology can eventually reach the point where computers are practical for solving the types of problem encountered in designing a complete aircraft using computer simulation. As an example of how far computer technology has progressed, 20 years ago it would have taken 30 years of computational time to perform the same calculations that can now be done in a few minutes.

Fig. 3-28. Radio-controlled models can be the first step in testing new aerodynamic concepts. This JW-1 RCM was used to try out the joined-wing idea. (Courtesy Julian Wolkovitch)

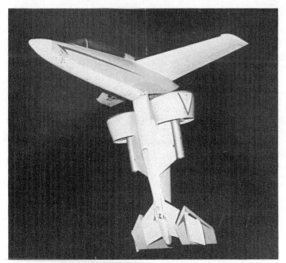

Fig. 3-29. This is one design for a V/STOL aircraft that you would want to try out in unmanned scale-model form before you build a man-rated model. Appropriately, it is called the nutcracker. (Courtesy Grumman Corporation)

One of the greatest expenses involved in building flight-test aircraft is in their man-rating, that is, incorporating the safety and life-support equipment for the pilot. Cost savings are now being realized by the use of sophisticated radio-controlled unmanned models called remotely piloted research vehicles. RPRVs can be built quite inexpensively and can be tested in flight regimes that could prove hazardous in a human-piloted test aircraft. For example, future concepts for fighters with super-maneuverability were flight tested with the HiMat RPRV, airdropped from a B-52 mothership and flown through some very demanding maneuvers by radio control. Other concepts, ranging from the joined wing to the new V/STOLs have also been tested in RPRV form (FIG. 3-29). Another advantage of RPRVs is that they can be easily modified to try out variations in a concept without the costly need to requalify the aircraft for manned flight.

4

Propulsion

Setting the Pace for Change

THROUGHOUT the history of aviation, propulsion technology has been the technology that has made milestone flights possible—from the Wright brothers' first flight to the Space Shuttle. In some cases, the lack of suitable powerplants has prevented attractive concepts from coming to fruition. Propulsion will still play this commanding role in the future.

While the Wright brothers recognized the advantages of the internal-combustion engine, they found that the available automobile engines were much too heavy. So they designed and built their own 12-horsepower engine with a power-to-weight ratio of 1-to-15, pretty good for its day. Similarly, they found propeller technology was insufficient, so again they used their aeronautical knowledge and native ability to design a very efficient propeller that represented a revolutionary advance in propellers.

Up until the jet age, the reciprocating engine was the most viable aircraft powerplant. Advances in internal-combustion engines came quite rapidly,

with most aircraft using radial, inline, or V-type cylinder layouts that were either air- or water-cooled. By the end of World War I, engine output had jumped to 400 horsepower in powerplants like the 12-cylinder Liberty engine, perhaps outpacing the fragile airframes they were attached to.

One of the major propulsion advances of the pre-World War II era was the supercharger. The supercharger compresses the thin air of high altitudes so engines can get sufficient amounts of air for proper combustion and can produce sufficient power. It first allowed military aircraft, and then commercial airliners, to fly at altitudes high enough to avoid most adverse weather. The supercharger also produced an important side benefit, the pressurized-cabin airliner. Both of these items can be attributed to making commercial air travel an everyday occurrence, starting with the pioneering Boeing 247 and Douglas DC-3 (both with supercharged engines) and the Boeing 307 *Stratoliner* (the first pressurized-cabin airliner to go into commercial service).

Incidentally, while most engine makers concentrated on superchargers driven by gears off of the engine crankshaft, General Electric in the U.S. worked on perfecting the turbosupercharger, or turbocharger. The latter is powered by hot gases through a turbine; it extracts power from the exhaust that normally would just be wasted out the exhaust pipe.

Even in the jet age, the low-cost and efficient internal-combustion engine is still, by far, the most popular powerplant for light and general-aviation aircraft and will be around well into the 21st century.

By the early 1950s, the piston engine had reached its zenith with the Wright Turbo-Compound, an 18-cylinder engine that could produce up to 3700 horsepower and allowed airliners like the Douglas DC-7 and Lockheed *Super Constellation* and *Starliner* to fly across the continent or the Atlantic Ocean nonstop. But jets were coming to supplant the internal-combustion engine in the high-performance military and large commercial airliner arenas.

By the end of World War II the jet-powered Lockheed P-80 *Shooting Star*, the Air Force's first combat jet, had made its maiden flight, and the jet age was here. By 1949 the first jet airliner, the de-Havilland *Comet*, was flying, but because of a series of unfortunate crashes traced to airframe structural fatigue, the *Comet* never received the fame and fortune it rightfully deserved. That would go to the Boeing 707, with its JT3C turbojet engines adapted from the jet engines used in such Air Force craft as the North American F-100 and Boeing B-52.

The turboprop, a spinoff of the pure turbojet, brought the jet age to the commuter and business aircraft markets. The turboprop was more suited to these markets because of its high thrust at low to medium subsonic speeds and good fuel economy in comparison to the fuel-thirsty turbojet. The turboshaft engine, a close relative of the turboprop, replaced the complex, heavy, and maintenance-intensive reciprocating engines that had powered all helicopters until the Kaman K-255 first flew in 1951. Lightweight, with less vibration and

noise, this small gas-turbine engine was popularized by the famous Bell *Huey* helicopters.

PROPULSION FOR HYPERSONIC FLIGHT

Our look into future propulsion systems begins with the applications that will place the greatest demands on technology, flight in the hypersonic regimes—Mach 5 and beyond. What makes these applications especially challenging is the fact that not only must the aircraft fly at very high speeds and operate at very high temperatures, but it must also be able to fly slow enough to take off and land on conventional airport runways. And to keep weights reasonable, as well as to reduce complexity, the goal is to do the entire job with a single engine-type called a combined-cycle engine.

For low-speed operation, the combined-cycle engine would operate like a normal turbojet (FIGS. 4-1 AND 4-2). As the aircraft accelerates it would operate like a ramjet, and then a scramjet. If the hypersonic aircraft is used for placing payloads into orbit, the combined-cycle could even be designed to operate as a rocket in space, where there is no oxygen. All of this would be done with a single engine, converting from cycle to cycle (thus the title combined-cycle) by varying the configuration and geometry of the air passages through the engine. This would require a rather elaborate control system.

In a turbojet engine, the incoming airflow is slowed down, both to convert the velocity to pressure (to provide thrust) and so that the fuel-air mixture can be ignited and burned in the combustion chamber. A compressor is needed in front of the combustion chamber to further increase the pressure, and a turbine section is located behind the combustion chamber to extract power from the exhaust gases to drive the compressor and various engine accessories. As flight speeds increase, the compressor and turbine can be eliminated to create a ramjet, in which the entire conversion of velocity to pressure is done by the ram effect without a need for any rotating machinery.

Unfortunately, as air is decelerated, its temperature rises. The faster the airplane travels, the more the air has to be decelerated, if a normal

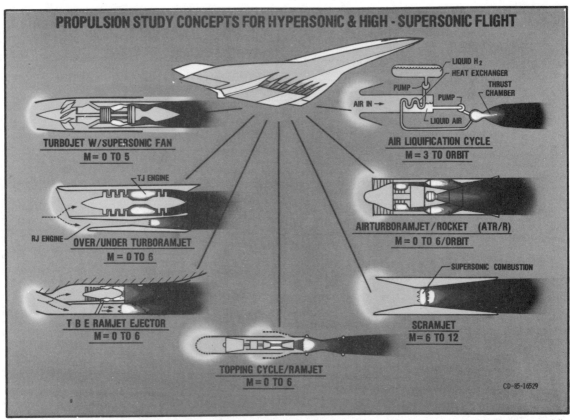

PROPULSION STUDY CONCEPTS FOR HYPERSONIC & HIGH - SUPERSONIC FLIGHT

TURBOJET W/SUPERSONIC FAN
M = 0 TO 5

OVER/UNDER TURBORAMJET
M = 0 TO 6

T B E RAMJET EJECTOR
M = 0 TO 6

TOPPING CYCLE/RAMJET
M = 0 TO 6

LIQUID H$_2$
HEAT EXCHANGER
THRUST CHAMBER
PUMP
AIR IN
PUMP
LIQUID AIR

AIR LIQUIFICATION CYCLE
M = 3 TO ORBIT

AIRTURBORAMJET/ROCKET (ATR/R)
M = 0 TO 6/ORBIT

SUPERSONIC COMBUSTION

SCRAMJET
M = 6 TO 12

TJ ENGINE
RJ ENGINE

CD-85-16529

Fig. 4-1. This shows how a combined-cycle engine would allow the National Aerospace Plane to take off, land, and fly at all speeds from low-subsonic to orbital velocities. (Courtesy NASA)

turbojet engine is used, and the higher its temperature becomes. The maximum speed of a turbojet is about Mach 3 to 3.5. Above these speeds, the temperatures inside the engine get so hot that metals within the engine lose their strength and can even melt. The ramjet with its few moving parts partially overcomes this problem, but it is also limited, with top speeds of Mach 5 to 6. The problem is that the air must still be decelerated to low-subsonic speeds for combustion to take place; excessive temperatures put a limit on top speeds.

The answer is the scramjet, in which the air can be mixed with fuel and ignited while still traveling at supersonic speeds. As a result, temperature increases and pressure losses due to shocks are greatly reduced. Because the scramjet works on the ramjet principle at supersonic speeds, the name

scramjet, short for supersonic combustion ramjet, is quite fitting.

The scramjet, however, brings along its own set of problems. One of these is the fact that, because the fuel-air mixture is moving so fast through the combustion zone, there is very little time for ignition and combustion to take place. Hydrogen is about the only fuel that has rapid enough ignition and combustion properties.

Even though the idea of the scramjet is quite simple and it essentially does not have any moving parts, it still represents a real technological challenge, one that engineers are only just beginning to get a handle on (FIG. 4-3). The U.S. aerospace community worked on the scramjet quite extensively in the mid-1960s, but dropped its development because sophisticated materials and wind

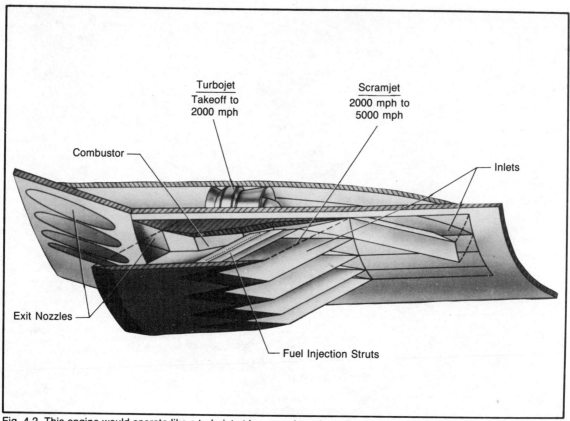

Fig. 4-2. This engine would operate like a turbojet at low speeds and a scramjet at high speeds. Unlike current engines that are often just attached to the aircraft's fuselage, the scramjet would be an integral part of the airframe, and the fuselage itself would be part of the inlet and nozzle. (Courtesy NASA)

tunnels were not yet available. Facilities are just now being constructed that can be used in the development of scramjets. The design and analysis of the scramjet requires tremendous computer power, well beyond that of the 1960s, but now available with the new generation of supercomputers.

Engineers are now confident that the scramjet is feasible. As of this writing, the scramjet has been tested at a maximum speed of about Mach 8, but computer studies have shown that the scramjet has the potential to operate at up to Mach 25, a speed required if the concept is to be used in a 21st-century version of the Space Shuttle.

Like the ramjet, the scramjet is not capable of accelerating itself from zero velocity. Indeed, the scramjet cannot really start operating before speeds of about Mach 6. Other propulsion devices are needed to get the scramjet up to its operating speed, thus the reason for interest in the combined-cycle mentioned earlier.

The combined-cycle engine would be fully integrated into the aerospace vehicle it powers, not just a powerplant attached to the airframe. For example, in hypersonic designs, the forward part of the lower fuselage would actually be the engine intake while the rear of the fuselage would function as an exhaust nozzle (FIG. 4-4).

ENGINES FOR HIGH-PERFORMANCE MILITARY AIRCRAFT

When it comes to somewhat more conventional powerplants, engines for high-performance military aircraft, particularly the Advanced Tactical Fighter (ATF), will lead the way, just as in the past.

Fig. 4-3. One module of a scramjet engine installed in a wind tunnel for testing at hypersonic speeds. (Courtesy NASA)

The ATF represents an evolutionary rather than a revolutionary improvement over current fighter engines, but it will incorporate much advanced technology, especially in materials and computerized controls.

The thrust-to-weight ratio of the ATF is expected to be twice that of current engines (so are many other factors, including cost, reliability, and maintainability). This ratio of 15-to-1 or even 20-to-1 means a lighter-weight fighter. For each additional pound of engine weight, several pounds are added to the total aircraft weight, due to the need for added structure and more fuel. Because aircraft operating costs can be directly correlated with aircraft weight, a lighter-weight aircraft is a less-expensive aircraft to operate.

Maneuverability is a key factor in survivability, and the ATF's high thrust-to-weight ratio is a major ingredient in maneuverability. The specifications for the ATF engine call for vectored- and even reversed-thrust capability to enhance maneuverability (FIGS. 4-5 AND 4-6 AND PLATE 3). High

thrust-to-weight ratios, coupled with vectored thrust, are important if advanced fighters are to have the short takeoff and landing (STOL) capability, needed to operate from damaged runways. The ATF will also have sustained supersonic cruise capability without using an afterburner.

The ATF engine will use the results of mid-1970s research to improve reliability and maintainability. This research showed that each full cycle of engine operation (from engine-off to full-thrust to engine-off) extracts a certain amount of life from the engine, which relates directly to the time between engine overhauls. Typically, engines built before 1985 can go about 900 full cycles between overhauls. The newest engines have doubled this, to some 1800 cycles, which is equivalent to about three years between overhauls. Engines currently being developed, like those for the ATF, are aimed at as many as 4000 cycles, which would more than double today's time between overhauls.

Part of this increase in engine life will come from new materials that will withstand the high stresses and temperatures found in critical areas of the compressor, combustor, and turbines. These materials are likely to include refractory metals, intermetallic compounds (e.g., titanium-aluminum and nickel-aluminum), and structural ceramics (such as silicon-carbide, silicon-nitride, and carbon-carbon composites). Thermal barrier coatings on turbine blades could offer greater resistance to high temperatures and extend turbine blade life. Finally, controlled-diffusion blades, with added thickness at both the leading and trailing edges, will not only resist corrosion but also improve reliability and fuel efficiency by reducing the number of blades needed.

Electronics will play a key role in engines of the future. The ATF engine will have sophisticated controls to eke out every bit of energy possible from each pound of fuel. To obtain peak performance at all operating conditions, sensors throughout the engine will feed performance data to an electronic fuel control system which will use the data to keep the engine operating within specified limits. Electronics will also be used to monitor engine condition and even diagnose problems. A fault detection system

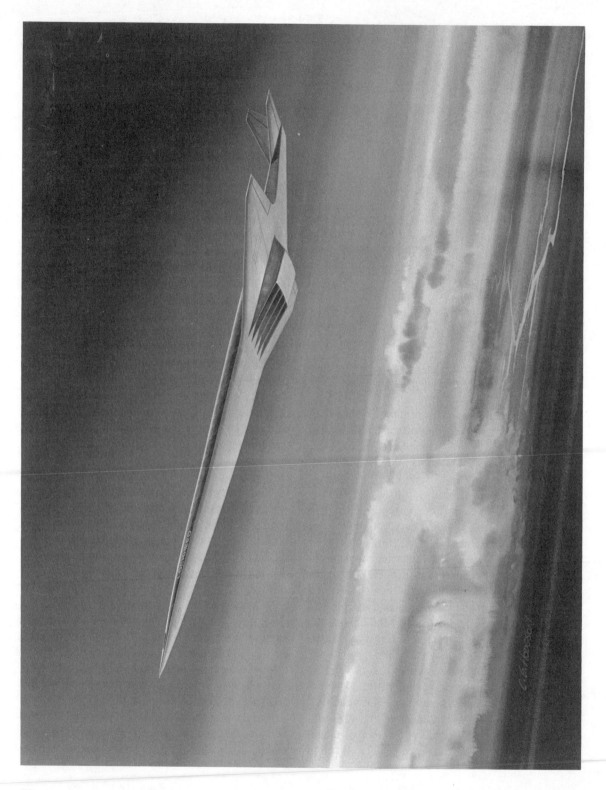

Fig. 4-4. Opposite: An artist's concept of a scramjet engine installed in a hypersonic transport. (Courtesy Lockheed-California Company)

to signal the presence of foreign material in the airstream could warn of abnormal wear and erosion problems.

Supercomputers are playing a significant role in the development of advanced engines. By using computer models, engineers can realistically try out new design ideas without the need for expensive testing in wind tunnels and other engine test facilities.

Even though the ATF is a turbojet, the technology being developed for the ATF will set the pace for all types of gas-turbine propulsion systems, including applications for turbofans, turboshafts, fanjets, and propfans. That is the way it has been in the past, and that is how it will be in the future.

PROPELLERS ARE HERE TO STAY

In their neverending search for more fuel-efficient engines, engineers have taken a renewed interest in the propeller. It is a well known fact that propellers on some large transports can achieve propulsive efficiencies of 85 to 87 percent. By comparison, the best of today's high bypass-ratio turbofan engines have efficiencies of 60 to 65 percent; even the advanced turbofans of the future will never be able to approach the efficiency of the propeller. As a point of history, the propeller designed by the Wright brothers for their 1903 aircraft had a

remarkable efficiency of 70 percent!

Unfortunately, the propeller-driven aircraft has been traditionally limited in its maximum speed, about Mach 0.6. As the speed of the aircraft approaches Mach 0.6, the airflow at the propeller tips reaches supersonic speeds and the efficiency drops drastically, not to mention a sizable increase in noise.

The renewed interest in propellers is centered around a new fuel-saving concept called the propfan, a design that appears to be quite practical now, mainly because of advances in materials technology. Indeed, the propfan may be the only radical change to be seen on commercial airliners and military transports of the 21st century. NASA has been working on the propfan for years and has more recently been joined in its effort by Boeing and General Electric (FIGS. 4-7 AND 4-8).

The appearance of the propfan differs substantially from propellers of the past. For starters, the propeller blades on the propfan are quite short. To provide the same amount of power many more blades will be used—8, 10, or even 12 blades may be common practice. The blades will be very thin with wide chords to increase the critical Mach number, the speed at which supersonic speeds are reached somewhere on the blade. They will also be highly swept, with a scimitar-like shape to further improve operation at high speeds. The blades will be made of advanced materials like composites and lightweight metallic alloys that offer both the high

Fig. 4-5. This is the PW5000 engine being developed for the ATF by Pratt & Whitney. Note the rectangular nozzle that will give thrust-vectoring capability for, among other things, STOL operation. (Courtesy Pratt & Whitney)

Fig. 4-6. Opposite: Rectangular nozzles installed on an F-15 for flight testing. (Courtesy McDonnell Douglas)

strength and low weight needed to keep centrifugal stresses down (FIG. 4-9).

The small-diameter blades offer other advantages such as a relatively small overall size, making for easier installation on the aircraft. This means the engines could be mounted at the rear of the aircraft and push rather than pull the aircraft.

The pusher configuration is inherently more efficient than the more conventional tractor engine arrangement, and rear-mounted engines reduce the problem of cabin noise, produce less drag, and allow higher ground clearance. Also, placing the engines closer to the centerline of the aircraft greatly improves aircraft control characteristics if the aircraft has to fly with an engine out. The yawing and pitching is reduced under such conditions and the

Fig. 4-7. A propfan engine with two sets of contrarotating blades. Note the large number of blades, their short length, and scimitar shape. (Courtesy General Electric)

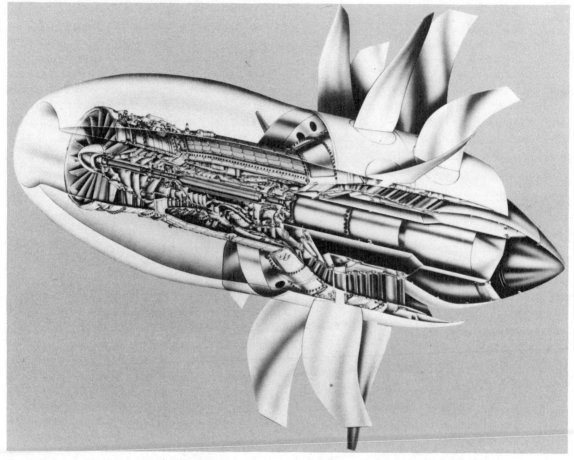

Fig. 4-8. A cutaway drawing of the inner workings of a propfan engine. (Courtesy General Electric)

need for excessively long fuselages and large tails to compensate for yawing is alleviated.

Engine manufacturers are considering designs with a single set of rotating blades as well as with two sets of smaller-diameter contrarotating blades (which can be installed close to the fuselage). Contrarotation also reduces gyroscopic effects and makes the engine even more efficient, perhaps about 10 percent more fuel efficient than a propfan with a single set of blades, if the engine is mounted at the rear of the aircraft. Unless a conventional wing-mounted propeller is carefully designed, most of its swirl energy is lost to the airstream. The propfan's high RPMs coupled with its small blade diameter results in a great deal of swirl energy. By placing a second set of contrarotat-

ing blades behind the first set, much of the swirl energy from the first set can be converted to useful thrust by the second.

Some advanced designs might incorporate a shroud around the propeller, effectively converting the propfan into a turbofan with a very high bypass ratio. The bypass ratio is a measure of how much air passes outside of the core of the engine (i.e., the compressor, combustor, turbine, and nozzle section), compared to the volume that actually passes through the core. Turbofans with relatively high bypass ratios are already used extensively on military and commercial aircraft because of their good fuel economy at high speeds. The ducted propfan would extend this advantage with a reduction in noise problems.

Fig. 4-9. Lasers have been used in wind tunnel tests to study the performance characteristics of propfan blades. (Courtesy NASA)

The technology from propfan development will be useful on all future aircraft with propellers. And propellers will remain the most popular means of converting engine power to thrust, whether they are matched to turboprop engines, in the case of business and commuter aircraft, or internal-combustion engines for light and pleasure aircraft (PLATE 17). These propellers, however, will take on new shapes and be made of new materials to make them more efficient, better performing, and quieter. Also, the sophisticated computer models developed for designing the new propfan engines will be adapted so that the best propellers can be designed for other types of engines.

PROPULSION FOR V/STOL AIRCRAFT

Nowhere else is thrust-to-weight ratio more

critical than in aircraft that take off and land vertically or in very short distances. For any craft to rise vertically, its thrust must exceed its weight, and to do it effectively, thrust must exceed weight by a rather wide margin. One of the big stumbling blocks for most V/STOLs of the past (and there were many attempts) was obtaining engines with sufficient thrust.

The first really successful V/STOL, the AV-8 *Harrier*, was developed by Hawker Siddeley (now British Aerospace) in England and performed superbly in the hands of the British pilots during the Falkland Islands conflict. What made the *Harrier* a success was the vectored-thrust Rolls-Royce *Pegasus* engine. The idea behind the vectored-thrust engine is quite simple. The engine has four nozzles, two at the front and two at the rear, which use exhaust gases to produce thrust in the normal fashion. The pilot can "vector" the thrust by swiveling the nozzles downward for vertical thrust and rearward for forward flight. He can also set them at intermediate positions or even rotate them a bit forward of vertical so the *Harrier* can perform its unique reverse maneuvers.

The *Pegasus* is able to accelerate the *Harrier* to over Mach 0.9, but not to supersonic speeds. To obtain supersonic performance, U.S. and British military planners, along with their airframe and engine contractors, are investigating ways to add supersonic performance to the *Harrier's* bag of tricks. Naturally, the most critical element here is the propulsion system.

Future supersonic V/STOL engines might utilize *plenum-chamber burning*. This consists of adding combustion chambers, the plenums, to the forward nozzles of *Pegasus*-type engines. Hot gases are exhausted from the front nozzles, rather than just cool air as in the current *Harrier* engine. In essence, plenum-chamber burning is very much like an afterburner on a conventional turbojet engine and, like an afterburner, would only be used when an extra burst of thrust is needed (e.g., when accelerating to supersonic speeds).

A variation on the *Pegasus* idea is the *remote augmented-lift system*. Here, the bypass-air bleed from the compressor section is ducted through the fuselage to remote locations on the aircraft where nozzles convert the bypassed air into downward thrust. The exhaust from the main nozzle would also be deflected downward. To reach supersonic speeds, the bypassed air exiting from the rear nozzles would augment the rearward main exhaust flow.

As its name implies, the *ejector augmentor system* uses the ejector principle to augment the downward thrust of the deflected main nozzles (FIG. 4-10). With an ejector, high-velocity airflow bleed from the compressor passes through several nozzles in a vertical duct. This high-speed air entrains slower-moving outside air, drawing it through the duct to produce additional vertical lift.

The *tandem fan* engine is a gas turbine engine with the fan portion separated into two sections by a transfer duct. The duct contains a shutoff valve and its own auxiliary air inlet system. For vertical flight, the shutoff valve is closed and air is diverted downward from the front fan through the combustion chamber to a nozzle located below the transfer duct. An auxiliary duct supplies air to the main portions of the engine during this mode of operation. In forward flight, the engine operates like an ordinary gas-turbine engine equipped with an afterburner.

V/STOL applications place some very demanding requirements on their engines. V/STOLs that use either tilting rotors or complete wings require rather complex transmission systems. If the engines are located in the fuselage, drivetrains must be used to transmit power to the rotors. If the engines are attached to the rotors, the engines must be interconnected by drive lines so that the aircraft can be safely flown if one engine fails.

V/STOLs that are equipped with some type of a rotor will most likely be powered by turboshaft engines because the turboshaft provides the best thrust-to-weight ratio in this type of application.

For V/STOL concepts that use an X-wing with circulation control, the propulsion system must not only supply the power to turn the rotor, but also provide the airflow for the circulation control. Propulsion is also needed for forward thrust when the rotor is locked into place; this might require a separate gas turbine engine.

THE ROTARY ENGINE

At one time the automobile industry predicted that the rotary, or Wankel, engine was the automotive powerplant of the future and spent vast sums of money on its development. But because of reliability problems and higher-than-expected fuel consumption, the engine lost its glamour for the automakers. By the 21st century, however, the rotary engine could stage a comeback in the business, commuter, and light aircraft market.

Most of the components in a rotary engine have rotary rather than reciprocating motion (FIG. 4-11).

Fig. 4-10. Opposite: A supersonic V/STOL could use an ejector system to achieve vertical lift. (Courtesy General Dynamics)

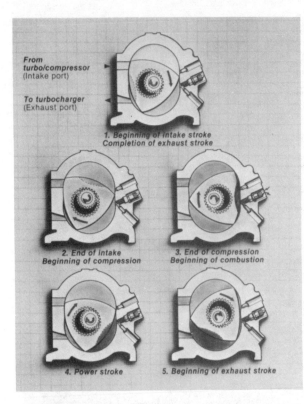

From turbo/compressor
(Intake port)

To turbocharger
(Exhaust port)

1. Beginning of intake stroke
Completion of exhaust stroke

2. End of intake
Beginning of compression

3. End of compression
Beginning of combustion

4. Power stroke

5. Beginning of exhaust stroke

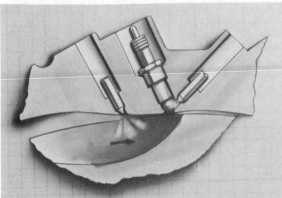

Fig. 4-11. The top figure shows how a rotary engine operates. The lower figure shows the twin combustion and injectors used for stratified combustion. (Courtesy Avco Lycoming)

There are no connecting rods, pistons, cams, valve trains, or other parts that move up and down. Thus, the rotary engine is not only much simpler with fewer components than reciprocating engines, it runs smoother and quieter—so quiet that airflow

and propeller noise will take the place of the engine as the primary contributors to cabin noise. The rotary engine is also virtually vibration-free and, being simpler, is theoretically more reliable and easier to maintain. Its lighter weight and smoother operation are ideal for helicopters and V/STOL aircraft.

Because the rotary engine produces three pulses for every turn of the rotor, high ratios of horsepower-to-displacement and horsepower-to-weight are the rule. Ratios of as high as 5-to-1 are projected for rotary engines of the future. (By comparison, a reciprocating engine that produces 1 horsepower per cubic-inch is considered very good.) The design of a rotary engine results in a smaller frontal area with less drag (FIG. 4-12). In essence, the rotary engine combines the simplicity, compactness, and high power-to-weight ratio of a two-cycle engine with the fuel economy and long, reliable life of a four-cycle engine.

While the rotary engine in itself shows promise, what really makes the engineers enthusiastic is *stratified-charge combustion*. With a stratified-charge engine there are essentially two sets of combustion chambers and (because the planned aircraft engines would be fuel-injected) two sets of injectors. One injector squirts a rich fuel-air mixture into a small combustion area where it is ignited by a spark plug. The burning rich mixture ignites a larger lean mixture that has been injected into the main combustion area by a second injector. While several conventional automobile engines use a version of stratified combustion, the rotary engine is especially amenable to this technique.

Considering the fuel concerns of the future, stratified combustion offers many advantages. First, it results in a more efficient engine, requiring less fuel and producing lower emissions. That is why automakers are using it already. For aircraft makers, the biggest advantage is that the engine can be modified to use any one of many fuels, including Jet A, aviation-grade gasoline, automobile-grade gasoline, liquid petroleum gas (LPG), alcohol, methane, or even diesel. A version used by commercial operators could burn jet fuel, another for the general-aviation market could burn automo-

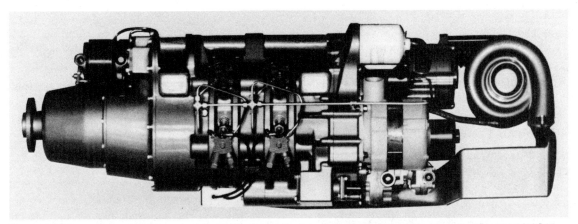

Fig. 4-12. This mockup of a rotary aircraft engine shows the low drag-producing profile possible. (Courtesy NASA)

bile gas, and a third, built for crop-dusters, would get by on LPG or diesel—fuels commonly found around the farm. The need for avgas, a fuel whose availability will undoubtedly dry up in the future, will be eliminated. Yet, because the engine uses a spark plug, cold weather starting with even diesel or jet fuel will not be a problem.

Aircraft rotary engines will be turbocharged for peak performance and will most likely be liquid-cooled. With liquid cooling, cabin heating can be more efficient (as in a car) and safer, compared to the normal procedure of taking heat from the exhaust manifold on air-cooled engines. Routing liquid coolant through the leading edges of the airfoils could result in an effective deicing system. Also liquid-cooled engines can make rapid descents from altitude, withstanding the sudden changes in air temperature.

While a single-rotor engine is possible, up to eight rotors can be stacked to obtain more power. Beyond that, the engine would become too long for aircraft use. For smaller commercial use, two stack-rotors with displacements of 200 cubic inches could produce 800 to 1000 horsepower.

The price of the rotary engine will probably be slightly higher than a comparable reciprocating engine, but only about one-third the cost of a turbine. Low fuel costs, however, would make up for the slightly higher initial cost.

Because the rotary is smaller and lighter, retrofitting current aircraft would be a solution to

future fuel availability problems. But for maximum payoff, new aircraft should be designed around the rotary engine's unique characteristics.

DIESEL ENGINES

An interesting contender for light aircraft, and even business and commuter aircraft, is the diesel engine. At first glance the idea of a diesel-powered aircraft may seem farfetched, but the concept has merit, and work on diesel aircraft engines has been underway at NASA and some engine manufacturers for several years. In fact, diesels flew in the late 1920s and early 1930s.

Forget your visions of the familiar heavy, smoky diesel that powers the lumbering 18-wheeler down the highway. The aircraft diesel engine is quite different while operating on the same diesel cycle. A well-designed, turbocharged, two-cycle diesel engine made of lightweight materials and running at high RPMs can produce just as much power per cubic-inch of displacement as the conventional gasoline engine. In addition, the aircraft diesel retains most of the characteristics that make it popular for ground transportation, including excellent fuel economy, rugged reliability, and fewer maintenance requirements. One of its primary attractions today is the fact that it uses fuel other than vanishing avgas. Diesel fuel is also safer to handle and is much less of a fire and explosion hazard in a crash.

Diesel engines have no problems with carburetor icing and no ignition system to interfere with aircraft avionics. While air-cooled diesels are quite possible, the high temperatures and pressures used in advanced aircraft diesels might favor liquid cooling and its previously mentioned advantages.

RECIPROCATING ENGINES

The conventional reciprocating engine, the most popular aircraft powerplant in terms of pure numbers, still has a lot of life left in it and will undoubtedly remain the most popular lightplane engine well into the 21st century. A truly more cost-effective engine that meets all the demands of the light airplane (or automobile, for that matter) has yet to be found. Also, engine manufacturers have invested huge amounts in production facilities that would have to be drastically modified or even scrapped if a radically new engine became popular.

Reciprocating engines, however, will be greatly improved through advances in technology. Some of the advances made in automobile engines will be adapted to the aircraft powerplant. The goals of the automaker and lightplane builder are quite similar when it comes to engines—make them more fuel-efficient and lighter-weight. Materials will play a key role in weight, with an abundance of non-metallic engine parts to be used in the future. Already several engines that use plastic parts extensively have been developed and tested.

The turbocharger is currently a "hot item" in both the aircraft and automobile industry. Today, turbochargers are added, essentially as an afterthought, to conventionally designed piston engines. In the future, to realize their full potential, turbochargers will become integral parts of the design. Already, both the advanced and diesel aircraft engines are designed around turbocharging.

Intercooling is one example of an improvement that can be made in turbocharged engines. When a turbocharger compresses intake air, heat is generated and the engine both loses efficiency and is subjected to excessive temperatures. About one percent of efficiency is lost for every 10-degree rise in temperature. The intercooler is a heat exchanger that cools the intake air using cool air from the airstream. There are two passageways in the intercooler. One carries the intake air from the turbocharger, cooling it before passing it to the engine. The other passageway carries cool outside air (which reduces the temperature of the air in the first passageway) and exhausts it back into the airstream at a higher temperature.

NUCLEAR ENGINES

For decades, engineers have proposed nuclear energy as the ultimate source of power for aircraft, but because of the high risk of radiation and nuclear contamination in an accident, most nuclear engine projects were abandoned early in their development. Advances in safer nuclear technologies might make such engines possible in the 21st century especially for application in extended airborne missions or in propelling very large transports very long distances. In these cases, more conventional engines with high thrust capabilities would be used for takeoffs, climbing, and landing, and the nuclear powerplants would be used for the "long haul." Experts believe safe nuclear engines that could produce large amounts of thrust and still be about the size of a 55-gallon oil drum are quite feasible. Convincing the general public of their safety might not be as feasible.

AVIATION FUELS OF THE FUTURE

Fuels are an important part of the story of future propulsion. Today, fuel accounts for a major share of an airline's direct operating costs. And although aviation uses less than 10 percent of the petroleum consumed in transportation, this share is expected to grow to almost 15 percent by the year 2000. In the long run, fuel prices will again spiral upwards, and fossil fuels are expected to eventually run out. The development of alternate fuels (and aircraft that can use them) is, therefore, an important task for researchers.

Of all potential energy sources, only three have been identified as real alternatives to Jet A: synthetic Jet A (Synjet), Liquid Methane (LCH_4), and Liquid Hydrogen (LH_2) (TABLE 4-1).

Table 4-1. Scorecard on Advanced Fuels.

	SYNJET	LIQUID METHANE	LIQUID HYDROGEN
Availability in far future	Limited	Limited	Global
Renewable resource	No	No	Can be
Production investment	Moderate	High	Very high
Production cost	Reasonable	Reasonable	Very high (now)
Effect on operating equipment	Little	New aircraft needed	New aircraft needed
Effect on airport fuel handling	Little	Major	Major
Noise (compared to now)	Same	Same	Reduced
Runway and equipment stress	Same	Same	Reduced
Pollution	Same	Same	Reduced
Safety	Same	Same	Improved

Synjet is very similar to jet-grade kerosene, except it is produced from coal, oil shale, or tar sands. Because its sources are fossil fuels, it is considered only an interim solution. There is also the problem of global availability, vital for worldwide airline operations. The U.S. is blessed with ample coal and oil shale deposits, unlike Western Europe and Japan which would have to import fuel (or the materials to produce fuel) at higher costs. Concerns have also been raised over the environmental pollution caused by strip mining of coal and recovery of oil shale.

Synjet's chief advantages are that it can be used in current engines (and with very little modification to fueling equipment) and can be produced at reasonable costs. However, unless there is a change in aircraft or airports, today's noise, runway loading, and air pollution would persist.

LCH$_4$ is manufactured from coal, shale oil, natural gas, and biomass and, thus, is also subject to problems of global availability. It could be available in more countries if it was produced from biomass, but it is considered only a transitional fuel, for the period between Jet A/Synjet A and the development of hydrogen-fueled aircraft.

Methane would most likely be produced and transported to airports in gaseous form where it would be liquefied into a high-density cryogenic form for use on the aircraft. Substantial investments would be required for liquefaction plants and

ground handling equipment, as well as retraining of personnel.

Studies have shown that, because of aerodynamic drag, insulation, plumbing, and weight-and-balance considerations, the optimal LCH$_4$ airliner would have large fuel tanks fore and aft of the passenger section. For the volume of LCH$_4$ required, the airplane would have spherical or nearly spherical tanks, and it would be a widebody, even for short-haul, 100- to 150-passenger configurations.

Because LCH$_4$ aircraft would probably be slightly larger than comparable kerosene-powered aircraft (on the order of 10 percent larger), problems with noise and airport accommodation would be increased somewhat. And pollution would still be a worry because LCH$_4$ is a carbon-based fuel.

The most promising fuel for the 21st century is liquid hydrogen. Its primary advantage is its global availability. It can be produced by numerous methods, many of which use renewable resources, and just about every country has some resources that could be turned into hydrogen. In several manufacturing methods the primary ingredient is water. Large quantities of energy, however, are required to convert water to hydrogen and to the cryogenic form needed for aircraft use. One technique is electrolysis, in which any abundant source of electricity (e.g., hydroelectric, nuclear, solar, ocean wave, wind, or geothermal) could be

Fig. 4-13. The liquid hydrogen for a hydrogen-fueled airliner would be carried in twin tanks and would require a widebody configuration. (Lockheed-California Company)

used. Nations with coal, oil shale, or tar sand resources could make liquid hydrogen with fossil fuels. Other advanced techniques use biomass.

Because of liquid hydrogen's low density and its need for cyrogenic storage, the LH_2 aircraft, like the LCH_4 aircraft, would use a widebody configuration with large fore and aft tanks (FIG. 4-13). But its high energy content more than compensates for the aircraft's size, so hydrogen-fueled aircraft can be as light as, if not lighter than, conventional aircraft.* While this shows up most dramatically on very large aircraft, it is still an important advantage for smaller ones. Lower weight means less noise, lower aircraft cost, and less stress on aircraft and runways.

In use, hydrogen poses no pollution problems; the products of hydrogen combustion are just water vapor, nitrogen, and small amounts of nitrous oxides. In production, however, pollution is still an important consideration, especially if carbon-based fuels are used.

The disadvantage of hydrogen is cost, both in capital investment and in processing. Today, there are no economical means to produce hydrogen in large quantities. As petroleum costs soar, the cost of producing hydrogen will become more competitive and the capital investment will be considered worthwhile. If fossil fuels are depleted, we will have no other choice than to turn to alternate fuels like hydrogen, regardless of the cost. Some experts already predict a "Hydrogen Economy" for the 21st century, and much research is underway to find economical production methods.

One factor that may push ahead the use of hydrogen-fueled aircraft is the development of the hypersonic aircraft, which will likely use hydrogen as fuel. Much of its technology and production facilities could be adapted for other military and commercial purposes.

In light of the *Hindenburg* disaster, at first glance, safety might seem to be a major problem with LH_2. The *Hindenburg,* however, used hydrogen in gaseous form, contained within rubberized cotton cells. In the case of an LH_2 aircraft it would

---

*A kilogram of hydrogen provides 2.80 times as much energy as a kilogram of Jet A. By comparison, a similar amount of LCH_4 supplies only about 1.16 times as much energy as Jet A. To fly a 400-passenger subsonic airliner on a 6300-mile flight would take about 250 tons of coal to produce the needed Synjet. By comparison, only about 200 tons of coal would be needed if LCH_4 were used, and this drops to less than 190 tons for LH_2.

be in liquid form, contained in welded metal tanks.

Granted, LH_2 is a high-energy fuel and must be handled accordingly, but safety experts give it high marks for safety, and in case of a crash, passengers and surroundings would be subjected to less hazard than with other types of aircraft fuels.

Interestingly, only about a dozen people were killed in the *Hindenburg* accident, yet it doomed the dirigible as a means of air transport. If the same logic had been applied to airline travel, people would not be flying today.

5

Avionics

THE HIGH TECHNOLOGY that will have the greatest impact on all aircraft of the 21st century will be in the area of avionics, the electronics used in aviation. Avionics started with simple radio voice-communication and took large leaps forward with military aircraft, missiles, and the space age. Nowhere else have the spinoffs from military and space technology advances been more rapid and widespread than in electronics. The explosion of electronic applications in the home, business, and automobile is phenomenal. Today, in many areas of electronic development, the tables have turned: electronics for business and commercial uses are coming first and are later adapted for military and commercial aviation.

Every sector of aviation will be affected by future advances in avionics. Advanced avionics can even be incorporated in old aircraft, often with no more difficulty than simple installation.

The possibilities for electronics are almost unlimited. While most commercial aircraft flying in the 21st century will look much like airliners in use today, and might, in fact, use today's airframes, even a casual look into the cockpits will reveal some major changes.

For the military, advances in electronics will not only mean new aircraft with new capabilities, but also existing aircraft with updated capabilities. One example of how electronics alone can change the characteristics of an aircraft is the new *Gripen* fighter being developed by Saab in Sweden. The *Gripen,* designed as a multipurpose aircraft for interception, ground attack and reconnaissance, can change roles merely by using different computer programs and weapons. Growth capability of the *Gripen* is ensured because new capabilities can be added through new computer hardware and software. This is a boon to countries like Sweden which cannot afford to develop, procure, and support different aircraft for different missions. This same philosophy will probably be adopted by other nations as the life-cycle cost of new aircraft continues to soar.

Avionics' impact will probably be felt greatest

in the general-aviation market. For greater safety, small aircraft will be required to carry rather sophisticated electronics. But the price of new electronics has a tendency to go down as the capabilities go up (the home computer is the best example of this). Avionics that now are found only in military and large commercial aircraft will become available to the pleasure flyer at reasonable costs.

THE BUILDING BLOCKS OF AVIONICS

The key technologies that will lead avionics development can be categorized into three broad areas: computers, optics, and artificial intelligence.

Computers

Future aircraft will require tremendous increases in computer power. To put the growth of computer power in perspective, let us start with current capabilities. Today, the Cray supercomputer, which represents the state-of-the-art as this book is being written, can perform 250 million calculations per minute or handle 40,000 instructions per second, three times faster than its predecessors. Yet the Cray had hardly reached the marketplace when Sandia National Laboratories announced a miniaturized version (FIG. 5-1). This computer, about the size of a car battery and weighing a few pounds, is small enough to fit aboard an aerospace vehicle. Most importantly, its cost would range from $75,000 to $200,000 compared to the $10 million or so for a laboratory-sized Cray.

The computer technology that promises great potential for future military (and even commercial) applications, ranging from aircraft to space satellites, is the very-high-speed integrated circuit (VHSIC) computer chip (FIG. 5-2). VHSIC development has an interesting history.

In the 1970s, the electronics industry turned its focus from the relatively small military market to the much more lucrative consumer market. Not only were the profits greater, but the demands were less stringent. Commercial applications usually did not require the computing power, testing, and quality control required in such applications as satellites, missiles, and high-performance aircraft. The

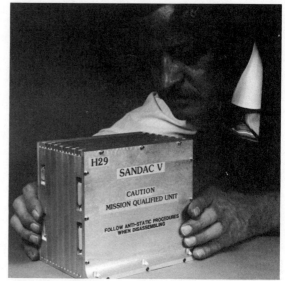

Fig. 5-1. The SANDAC V computer packs tremendous computing power in a small package. (Courtesy Sandia National Laboratories)

situation reached the point where the military had to use computer technology developed for the civilian market—usually quite a while after it was available to commercial users (because of the modifications and extra testing needed).

The U.S. military finally recognized that American superiority in computer technology was falling behind the needs of future system requirements. Thus, in 1980, the Department of Defense launched a high-priority, billion-dollar program to develop the VHSIC chip for use by all the military services. Because the VHSIC program is an 11-year program, the fruits of the investment will not start to be seen until the 1990s and beyond.

But what capabilities VHSIC computers will have! They will be able to make 2 to 12 billion calculations per second—10 to 100 times faster than the fastest chips available in the early 1980s. In addition, their size, weight, electrical power, failure rate, and life cycle costs will decrease to a fraction of today's standards. For example, a 50-pound computer used for data processing aboard an aircraft today could be reduced to a mere three pounds using VHSIC technology. The bottom line for the military is such increased capability as 50-times-

Fig. 5-2. The very high-speed integrated circuit (VHSIC) computer chip represents a major technology advance for future avionic systems. (Courtesy TRW)

faster radar, 100-times-faster weapons targeting, and up to 200-times-faster electronic warfare systems. Because these systems will be designed specifically for military applications, they will incorporate features for survivability on the modern battlefield, including immunity to radiation and electromagnetic pulses.

Although VHSIC technology will find greatest application in future aircraft—in fact some concepts would not be possible without it—they will also be used to update current military aircraft. Plans are to use VHSIC technology in current Air Force fighters such as the McDonnell Douglas F-4 and F-15 and the General Dynamics F-16. Eventually,

VHSIC technology will permeate everything from airplanes and missiles to submarines and helicopters, as well as satellites and ground-based communication systems. The applications are virtually unlimited.

While on the subject of computer chips, mention should be made of breakthroughs in their materials. Up to now, computer chips have used silicon, but chips made of gallium arsenide (GaAs), may be ready to provide some stiff new competition. GaAs has long tantalized electronics designers with its promise of much greater speed, greater tolerance to large temperature changes, and ability to absorb more radiation without any deterioration. But it has also frustrated them with its fragility and production difficulties. Now, the GaAs chip is ready to come out of the laboratory and onto the production line. Of course, the first application will probably be in military computers but commercial and general-aviation applications will come later.

The key to super speed is how the chips are integrated. Time-saving, efficient, computer architectures and large memory capacities allow high-speed chips to work at their maximum speed. One important advance, parallel computing, allows several processors to work on a problem at the same time. This requires some sophisticated componentry to make the various processors work in unison without wasting time in exchanging data or programs.

As important as the computers themselves are, the software that turns rather inanimate electronics into problem-solving brains is of equal importance. Often, as much or more is invested in computer programming for a new system as is invested in the hardware. For aerospace applications, much of the cost of a new program is in checking it out under virtually all possible operational situations. When safety or mission accomplishment is involved, the possibility of a "bug" in the computer software cannot be tolerated.

Future aircraft will use not one, but several computers. Not only must they communicate with one another, they must be able to interact with computers aboard other aircraft, space satellites (that might be providing communications and navigation information), and computers on the ground.

To add to the complexity of the problem, military and commercial flight operations are often international in nature. Like people conversing, computers must share a common language. The computer community, therefore, has expressed great interest in adopting a common language for future computer systems. The language of current interest, at least within the Department of Defense, is called ADA.

Optics

Systems that use the special properties of light represent the next revolution in avionics. Already

the laser is found in aviation applications ranging from laser gyroscopes for navigation to laser range finders for accurately aiming weapons at targets. But this is the tip of the iceberg for optic-based avionics.

Fiber optics is one of the most promising of the newly emerging technologies. Amazingly large amounts of information can be transmitted at the speed of light along fiber optic strands no larger in diameter than a human hair. The information is in the form of pulses of light called photons and is sent in a manner akin to a flashlight sending Morse code down a long piece of pipe. With fiber optics the light source is the laser, and many messages can be transmitted simultaneously by using different frequencies of light. In theory at least, it would be possible to transmit all of the world's telephone conversations on a single optical fiber. And the speed of photonics, as this new technology is called, is such that the entire contents of the Library of Congress could be transmitted in a few seconds.

The potential for photonics in the aerospace community is almost unlimited. For example, fiber optics, along with the laser, form the basis for fly-by-light aircraft flight-control systems. They are lighter and consume less power than even fly-by-wire systems. In addition, they are unaffected by electromagnetic interference and, therefore, cannot be jammed and will continue to operate in a post-nuclear environment. They are also virtually immune to corrosion.

Later applications of photonics might include optical computers that could operate thousands of times faster and more efficiently than today's microchip-based machines. Optical scanners that can "interpret" photo imagery would have important applications in reconnaissance. Some of the experts even believe that photonics are as technologically revolutionary as the transistor was in the 1950s.

Artificial Intelligence

Another technology that will revolutionize the aerospace and computer community is artificial intelligence (AI). The term artificial intelligence was coined in 1956, and the idea itself has been around since 1947. Artificial intelligence is that branch of computer science that attempts to use computers to solve problems in a manner that simulates the human reasoning process, in other words, to "think." Indeed, early AI investigations were concerned with designing the computer to mimic the physiological workings of the brain. With the brain as complex as it is, little headway was made until the research was reoriented towards imitating how the brain reasons.

Of all the approaches to AI, such as machine vision, machine reasoning, natural language, and expert systems, the last shows the greatest promise, especially in assisting pilots. In an expert system, computer data bases in a memory bank contain as much knowledge on a subject as can be compiled. In other words, the system is an "expert" on a particular subject and can be consulted by less knowledgeable experts, or even non-experts, to do a job or make an assessment of a situation. For example, the expert data base in a cockpit system might include such information as engineering and system data, weather and navigation, threat assessments, and the seasoned judgment of experienced pilots. The actual decision making is done using a "rule-of-thumb" approach based on expert experience. Decisions are made differently from the conventional right-or-wrong method of a binary computer. The expert system need not offer an absolute answer but can indicate the preferable alternative—the one with the highest probability of being correct—thus imitating the decision-making process of the human brain.

In an increasingly complicated and high-risk combat environment, military pilots need all the help they can get, so the military is investing vast resources in a form of AI called the Pilot's Associate (PA). PA serves as an additional aircraft "crewmember," handling much of the workload. For example, when a fighter detects and engages the enemy, the PA would recommend the most effective attack profile for the aircraft and its weapons. It could preset the weapons while positioning the aircraft for the best attack advantage, and if commanded, could even execute the attack. Throughout the engagement, the PA could increase survivability by recommending and, if desired, even executing appropriate defensive countermeasures and evasive maneuvers. However, as in all AI application, the pilot would still have complete override capability.

AI also offers many ways to help the commercial pilot overcome his ever-increasing workload and could well be the answer to future concerns for safer air travel and more cost-efficient airline operations, the two key factors that influence commercial aircraft makers and airlines to invest in new technology.

Today, the amount of information presented to the flight crew is enormous, and with advanced system sensors, computer-generated displays, and multifunction cathode-ray tubes, the volume of information available for making decisions will grow tremendously. Unfortunately, the brain's capability to absorb and digest data, and to make critical decisions based upon all the data, has not changed. This is where AI comes into the picture.

For example, an expert system can integrate, prioritize, and filter data, and then communicate only the most significant information in the context of the current situation. Most importantly, the system would provide the pilot with its best estimate of the situation and the recommended course of action, or several alternatives. The pilot could override the AI system if he had additional information bearing on the problem or if, based on his experience, he disagrees with it. Or he could interrogate the system to obtain more information.

A pilot can become so busy interpreting information that he can overlook a critical decision factor, especially when he is under stress, such as during an inflight emergency. Some accident reports have shown that flight crews were presented sufficient information to avert crashes, but for a variety of reasons did not use it. The pilots might not have been aware of degrading flight conditions, altitude, or attitude. Vital information might not have been displayed properly, integrated with other important data, or in a readily understandable form. It also could have been presented at the wrong time; perhaps, by the time all of it was finally interpreted, it was too late. Or the critical information might have been missed because the crew was too busy doing other routine things. An expert system acts as a very efficient "executive assistant."

Expert systems will "think ahead." Based on experience programmed into their software, they would keep track of critical situational and aircraft parameters and determine when the aircraft is on a collision course with another aircraft. The crew could then take corrective action before it is too late. The AI system would use its data base to determine a deviation from a nominal flight path and even determine the reason for the deviation. Then it would warn the crew, which could act on the information or ignore it. The system would project the results of continuing the current course and, if safety is in jeopardy, would issue a further warning and suggested course of action. If the warning is ignored, the system would be persistent enough to present the minimum recovery margin and even a "countdown" to let the pilot know that if he does not make changes or acknowledge the warning, the system will implement the recommended action at "time zero." Incidentally, AI systems would be extremely adaptive to pilot command preferences. For example, they could be customized to handle visual or aural warnings, manual or voice commands, or whatever combination the crew is most comfortable with.

The limitation of human reasoning can also cause a pilot to make a sequential error (i.e., leave out an important step in a multi-step process), or a capture error (i.e., use an old, familiar procedure instead of the needed new one). With AI a pilot would need to remember and execute only the first step in a complex procedure—the system would handle the rest. AI can also perform boring monitoring tasks; when a pilot's input is required he would be alerted and could then take over the vital functions requiring human decision making.

AI-based fault-diagnosis systems offer some interesting possibilities. Besides identifying a problem, diagnosing the fault, and determining its effect on the flight, an AI system could actually reconfigure the malfunctioning components, working around the difficulty so that the flight could be safely continued.

Much technology needs to be developed, however, before AI is a reality in the fighter or commercial airliner cockpit. Foremost is the tremendous amount of computer power required to be packaged in units that will fit in the cockpit. Then there are the very sophisticated software packages that must assimilate all the data required for an expert system to present intelligent choices to the pilot.

COCKPITS OF THE FUTURE
Airliner Cockpits

While some new avionics will have to wait for entirely new airliners, others will be incorporated into airliners that are flying today, as soon as it becomes technically and economically feasible.

In the 21st-century airliner cockpit, sidestick controllers, like those found in fighters, could replace the familiar control wheel and yoke (PLATE 16). With fly-by-wire or fly-by-light control systems the mechanical advantage provided by conventional control yokes is no longer needed. Elimination of these controls will greatly improve the visibility of the control panel, free up space for other controls and instruments, and enhance controllability with minimum physical exertion (FIG. 5-3). Some sidestick controllers work much like the "joystick" in video games. Others do not move but sense the varying pressure exerted by the pilot and translate this into changes in aircraft motion via the flight-control system.

Although not electronically related, another change will be windshields that improve the view of the outside world, important in collision avoidance. For example, future windshields could be one-piece, made of strong plastics that could better withstand bird strikes.

The biggest changes will be found on the instrument panel. Advanced panels will be designed with greater concern for ergonomics to greatly reduce workload. Until quite recently, flight decks grew in a rather hodge-podge manner through the replacement of outdated components and instruments with more modern ones as they became available. This resulted in a conglomeration of

Fig. 5-3. This is a mockup of a future airliner cockpit designed to decrease pilot workload. (Courtesy Lockheed Georgia)

knobs, switches, and electromechanical displays contributing to excessive crew workloads and, possibly, misinterpreted information. The Electronic Flight Instrumentation System (EFIS) now appearing on the commercial avionics market will go a long way in correcting this problem. With the EFIS, all flight and performance information can be displayed on a few cathode-ray tubes.

You will not have to wait until the 21st century to see the EFIS in the cockpit. Airlines are already beginning to integrate the EFIS into current airliners, and more will be used as their cost comes down. Eventually, even the traditional instruments now used as backups for the CRTs will be gone, and the flight deck could look like a modern office, complete with small desks at each crew station.

The key part of the EFIS is the computer-generated graphic display. Rapid advances in computer graphics, the results of the exploding personal and industrial computer markets, are being applied to cockpit displays. Multicolor, high-resolution displays are at hand. CRTs with multiple windows that can display a variety of information simultaneously (eliminating the need to scroll through computer menus) are already available. This is important to a pilot, who needs a variety of information instantaneously. The almost limitless potential for computer graphics includes computer-generated maps, route and destination charts, and real-time multicolor weather displays.

As modern as current CRTs may seem to be, they will probably be replaced eventually by flat-panel displays (FIG. 5-4). Conventional CRT displays take up more than a foot of space behind the instrument panel. U.S. and foreign electronics companies are now developing flat-panel displays that will use less than a quarter of that space.

The instruments on the flight deck of the 21st-century airliner will show great strides toward safety and economy. Avoiding midair near-misses is of great importance, and systems are now being developed to help the pilot. For example, there is the Traffic Alert and Collision Avoidance System (TCAS). TCAS requires transponders to be installed in cooperating aircraft. TCAS then interrogates the transponders in all nearby aircraft. From the responses, TCAS can compute their range, altitude, and bearing. If one of these aircraft is in the airliner's airspace, the pilot is warned both visually and aurally. The pilot is also given instructions on the least-disruptive maneuver to make to assure adequate separation. Additionally, TCAS can also continuously display traffic data on the weather radar screen to aid the pilot in tracking his airborne neighbors.

The Wind Shear Detection/Alert System (WSDA) is another important safety device. When WSDA detects an unsteady air mass, it gives the crew an amber wind-shear warning. If conditions are really severe, a red light goes on and an alarm sounds. Tests have shown that this type of system can detect wind shears in more than sufficient time for the crew to take corrective action. Fortunately, you will not have to wait until the next century to see systems like TCAS and WSDA. They should be in common usage by the end of this decade.

After safety, maximum profitability is next in importance to the airline operator. Thus, systems like the Flight Management Computer System (FMCS) will become an integral part of the flight deck. FMCS uses a computer (integrated with the autopilot and engine controls) to obtain optimum fuel economy and overall aircraft operating efficiency.

Military Cockpits

When it comes to cockpits in fighters, bombers,

transports, helicopters, and V/STOL for the military, as the saying goes, "you ain't seen nothin' yet."

The Head Up Display (HUD) is already the way of life in high-performance military fighters. HUDs display important information from the engine, flight-control, navigation, and weapons-control systems on a small screen in front of the pilot. The clear HUD screen is located so that the pilot can see information without taking his eyes off the outside world. This capability is extremely valuable during the heat of combat. However, HUDs are not just for the fighter pilot. Various versions are finding their way into airliner cockpits, and lower-cost models could become a hot item for business and pleasure pilots.

The Virtual Cockpit takes the idea of the HUD one step farther. In combat, a pilot needs a 360-degree view to keep track of both targets and threats; at the same time he needs instantaneous information on critical aircraft parameters. With the Virtual Cockpit, the HUD is moved to the pilot's helmet so it moves as the pilot looks around.

With the Virtual Cockpit's Helmet-Mounted Display (HMD), the pilot is presented with a panorama of information from the aircraft's sensors and avionics, organized both in time and in three-dimensional virtual space (FIG. 5-5). This display might be produced by miniature cathode-ray tubes mounted on the pilot's helmet and projected through the visor optics into the pilot's field of view. Head-tracking technology could determine where the pilot is looking at a particular instant so that the data could be pointed in the direction he wishes to view. A critical technology item here will be a helmet that can handle all the optics and electronics and still be light and comfortable enough to wear for long periods.

But HUDs and Virtual Cockpit displays could present more than just information about aircraft systems. Using sensors like forward-looking in-

Fig. 5-4. Opposite: In this artist's concept of the ATF cockpit, note the six flat-panel color displays, including the center three that give the pilot a panoramic view of the tactical situation. (Courtesy Lockheed California)

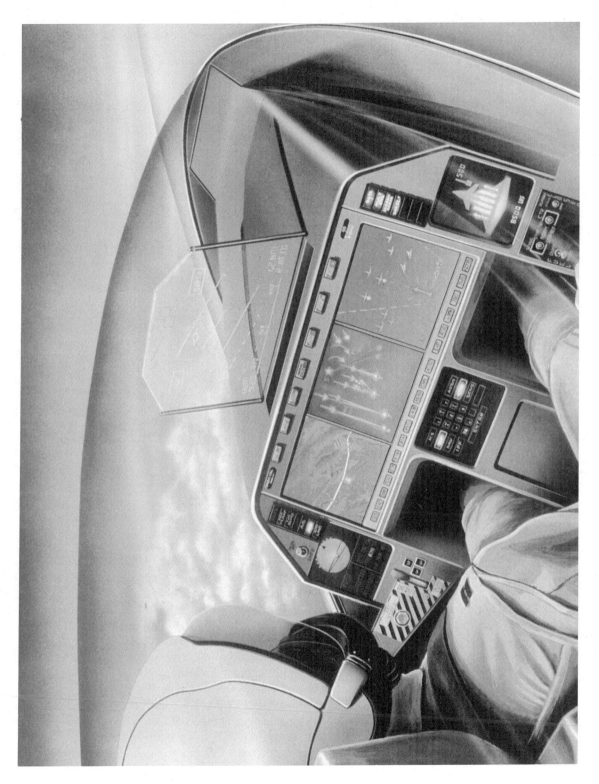

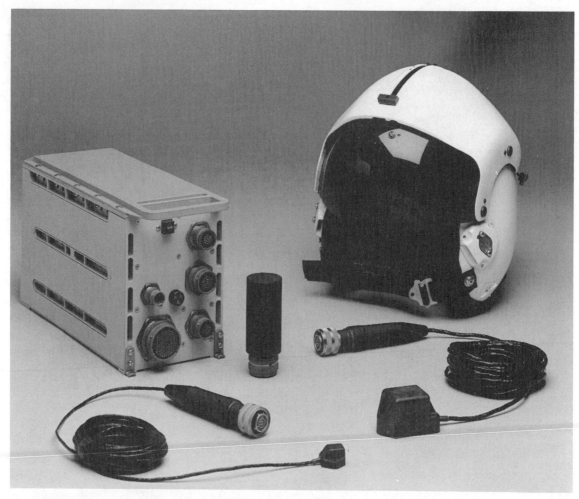

Fig. 5-5. This helmet-mounted display keeps track of the direction a pilot is looking. In essence, the pilot can detect, track, and destroy a target merely by looking at it. (Courtesy Polhemus Navigation Sciences)

frared cameras, a pilot could "see" through rain, fog, snow, and darkness by viewing an electronically-produced image of the scene outside. When he breaks out of the clouds there would be a harmonious blending of the electronic image with the real picture. You can probably see why this idea has been dubbed the "Magic Window." Such a system would not only be great for military pilots who must fly in all types of weather, but also for commercial carriers.

An even more advanced concept is called the "God's-eye view." Here the pilot would be presented with a big-picture view of his combat sit-uation. Projected on the HUD or HMD, the view would be the one he would see if he were located at a point outside the airplane, such as above and behind his aircraft. He would get a better image of threats, friendly aircraft, targets, and ground systems and his relation to them.

Because of the intense workload in future aircraft cockpits, voice control will be of great help. Pilots will be able to use verbal commands to operate cockpit functions, such as dialing radios and selecting weapons to be fired. The pilot will only have to speak the appropriate word into the microphone and watch the appropriate CRT or flat-panel display to determine that the verbal command was executed. Voice control could be coupled to the Virtual Cockpit so that the pilot would only have to look at a switch or display and utter a word or two to make things happen.

To make voice commands work, prior to a flight, each pilot would personally record the voice commands he will be using on a cassette tape which he will carry into the cockpit. The tape would be loaded into the data-transfer module, in reality a high-tech tape recorder. The module would be connected to the voice-command computer which would prepare individual word templates from the tapes. Each template serves as a master for recognizing the unique voice commands of a particular pilot. Before executing a command, the voice processor would instantaneously match the pilot's command with the prerecorded word on the template. If a match occurs, the computer would activate the appropriate control. One of the difficulties with voice controls is the fact that in stressful situations, such as in the heat of combat or during an emergency, the pilot's speech pattern could change dramatically. Sophisticated voice-recognition technology, therefore, would be required.

General-Aviation Cockpits

General-aviation aircraft often fly in and out of small airports that may not even have a control tower. In the future, these airports could have completely automated traffic-control systems that could provide pilots with vital information on weather conditions, airport characteristics, and air traffic without a single human involved. Radars would track air traffic, and weather sensors would gather climatic data. This information would be fed into a minicomputer that would convert it to voice-synthesized reports that would be transmitted on an assigned radio frequency. Several times a minute, a pilot could get the tail number and location of all aircraft within a 3- to 5-mile radius of the airport. Every few minutes, weather information would be broadcast, along with airport advisories that would identify the airport and list its active runways. Such a system, which has already been successfully tested in prototype form, could make flying into and out of small airfields much safer, and could do it without high labor cost. Alternatively, the same information could be displayed on a CRT on the instrument panel (FIG. 5-6).

Fig. 5-6. The flight deck of the *Starship I* represents the state-of-the-art for general-aviation aircraft. (Courtesy Beechcraft)

SENSORS

Sensors are the "eyes and ears" of an aircraft. They can be as simple as a pitot tube, which measures airspeed, or as complicated as an infrared camera, which can "see" in total darkness. A multitude of sensors are needed to generate the information presented to pilots on CRTs and video screens.

Many of the advances in sensor technology will center around techniques that will allow aircraft to fly and fight in less-than-ideal conditions. For example, the forward-looking infrared cameras, unlike radars, are passive sensors that do not emit radiation that could be detected by the enemy. And while radars will still be a primary form of sensor, new radars will operate at millimeter wavelengths, where they can see through the fog, rain, and smoke that clutters normal radars.

The wing and fuselage surfaces of the future aircraft could serve as integral parts of avionics. Sensors and antennas could be embedded in an aircraft's Kevlar and fiberglass skin. For example, VHSIC microcircuits could be etched on the skin surface by using photographic techniques.

By combining the microcircuits, sensors, and antennas embedded in the skin with other advanced technologies such as fiber optics, the aircraft skins will be able to "sense" and "communicate," in any direction and over a wide frequency band. Such a design would be a natural for Stealth aircraft because it would eliminate protruding electronic pods and domes that produce radar signatures. Smart skins could also reduce the weight and size of avionics systems, thereby increasing the number of systems an aircraft could carry and decreasing the aircraft's size.

HELP FROM SPACE

Military missions are already heavily dependent upon information gained from orbiting spacecraft. However, now most of the information must pass through ground terminals before it reaches the ultimate user in the cockpit of a fighter, bomber, or transport. This will change in the future. Navigation, intelligence, weather, and other data will be transmitted directly from satellite to aircraft, eliminating critical time delays. As equipment costs fall, this capability will be available to commercial users and then to the general-aviation population.

The first of these satellite systems that can "talk" directly to aircraft is the NAVSTAR global positioning system developed by Rockwell International for the U.S. Air Force (FIG. 5-7 AND PLATE 20). NAVSTAR lets its users know their position to

Fig. 5-7. A constellation of many satellites like the GPS NAVSTAR's would be required to provide continuous information to aircraft in the sky. (Rockwell International Satellite Systems Division)

within tens of feet, speed to within inches per second, and time to within a fraction of a millionth of a second. The keys to NAVSTAR's accuracy are its atomic clocks that lose or gain only one second every 300,000 years.

Although it is being developed for the Air Force, NAVSTAR will be used by all U.S. military services, on land, at sea, and in the air, as well as by commercial users. In fact, it can be used by anyone who has the need for precise navigation information, such as in air traffic control, search and rescue operations, land mapping, air and sea travel, and space operations. The required user equipment consists of an antenna, receiver, signal processor, controls, and display unit; such equipment can be installed in the smallest of aircraft. NAVSTAR, being a passive system just like the stars, can be used simultaneously by an unlimited number of users, and they do not reveal their locations when they use the system. NAVSTAR can be used under any type of weather condition.

The complete NAVSTAR system consists of an 18-satellite constellation circling the earth at 12,500 miles. This altitude and total number of satellites was chosen so that four of the satellites— the number of satellites that must be used simultaneously—are "visible" to users everywhere on Earth. The user's onboard equipment automatically computes the user's precise latitude, longitude, altitude, velocity, and time.

Incidentally, automakers are also looking at ways NAVSTAR might be used to help the motorist "navigate." If such systems were to be produced in the quantities required for cars, the cost of aircraft versions would certainly go down.

Much more information of value to pilots could eventually be obtained directly from space. Up-to-the-minute weather information could be transmitted from meteorological satellites directly to CRTs in the cockpit. Someday, air traffic controllers will depend on radars and other sensors aboard space satellites to keep track of air traffic and will use communication satellites to transmit messages, both by voice and picture, directly to the pilots. Someday, the entire system could be automated with computers, computer-generated graphics and voices, and voice recognition systems replacing human operators.

PUTTING IT ALL TOGETHER

In the past, aircraft have pretty much relied on separate equipment for individual functions, such as radars, communications, navigation, etc. Avionics seemed to be stuffed into airframes almost as an afterthought. This led to duplication of parts and excessive weight, cost, complexity, and maintenance problems.

In the future, an aircraft's avionics will be designed as an integrated package able to interact with artificial intelligence concepts to provide integrated, timely, and easy-to-understand information to the crew on its CRTs and HUDs. Common components will be used wherever possible, which will not only reduce the required inventory of spare parts, but will also lead to lower costs due to larger production runs. Black boxes that weigh up to 60 pounds will be replaced by video-cassette-sized modules that weigh about a pound. By using self-diagnosing avionics, the crew will be alerted when a particular module is malfunctioning and might even be able to replace it with a spare diskette stored aboard. Maintenance people will have an easy job identifying faulty avionics and can make repairs by slipping in a new module. Fewer connectors and cables will be needed to tie systems together, reducing weight and increasing reliability.

Self-healing avionics are an important step towards increased ability to complete missions. By using common components, it will be possible to automatically reconfigure the avionics so that the electronics of another system can be substituted for the broken component to keep things going.

Many of these new concepts in avionics are already being developed under an Air Force-sponsored program called *PAVE PILLAR* and will be an integral part of the Air Force's new Advanced Tactical Fighter.

SIMULATORS

Because of the expense of flying aircraft for

training and practice, simulators that closely duplicate actual flight without leaving the ground will be used increasingly in the future. Also, many new design concepts will be tested on ground-based or airborne simulators.

Flight Simulators

Flight simulators have come a long way from the Link Trainer of World War II fame. Today, fledgling pilots can gain much of their training in very sophisticated simulators. Experienced pilots can maintain their proficiency without burning up expensive fuel and can even be upgraded to fly new aircraft by doing most of their training in a simulator (FIGS. 5-8 THROUGH 5-12).

Combat missions can be simulated so that expensive ammunition and missiles need not be wasted in training and the aircrew can be given immediate feedback on their "gunnery" scores. By teaming up pairs of simulators, it is possible to practice air-to-air combat.

Simulators allow crews to practice emergency procedures that are too dangerous to attempt in a real aircraft. You would not want to practice flying a supersonic fighter with a broken rudder or landing a commercial airliner with its wheels up. But these are easily done with a simulator, and if you crash, you merely press the reset button and try again until you get it right. Also, by recording the simulation, the pilot can see a replay of mistakes that might have been made.

Pilots of Stealth-type aircraft could do most of their practice in simulators. Because one of the objectives of low-observable aircraft is to conceal their characteristics from potential enemies, Stealth aircraft cannot be flown in view of the public, especially on takeoffs and landings when cameras could record the aircraft's key design features. Stealth aircraft with low radar signatures present a real problem. These aircraft would practically be invisible on air traffic control radar screens and might not be seen by pilots of other aircraft sharing their airspace. One solution is to equip the Stealth aircraft with "training" radar reflectors that would give a false, but visible, radar signature during training flights. Another approach is to do just

about all the training on sophisticated simulators.

Simulators are becoming more sophisticated to give pilots the most realistic simulation possible. With simulators that move, aircrews can experience all the sensations of actual flight, such as buffeting in turbulence, maneuvering in combat, and rough landings. Using special "G" suits and seat cushions that inflate and deflate rapidly, large acceleration forces can be simulated. Tape recordings and loud speakers duplicate normal sounds heard in the cockpit, and computers can synchronize things so every sensation happens at the precise instant for a realistic simulation.

The sense of sight represents the greatest challenge to the simulator designer, for it is the sense most difficult to "fool." For years, the "view" outside the simulator's cockpit window was generated by moving a TV camera around a carefully constructed scale model that included buildings, trees, bridges, and so forth. The camera moved in response to computer commands so that the scene presented was exactly and instantaneously correct for the attitude of aircraft, and it moved at a rate that corresponded to the aircraft's airspeed. The problem with this model-board technique was that the models were very tedious and expensive to build, and new boards had to be built to simulate new environments.

Recently, these models have been replaced by computer graphics. This technique requires tremendously large computer data bases and ultrahigh-speed computers to create pictures that change at rates of 50 to 60 frames per second. Most computer-generated scenes start with topographic maps. Then realistic details like airports, roads, railways, bridges, and even individual trees and rocks are added, either by hand or by computer duplicating techniques.

Unfortunately, even the best computer-generated graphics are somewhat abstract and unrealistic in appearance, so scientists are working on simulators that use aerial photographs stored on videodisks. Literally thousands of photos, up to 50,000 on each side of a disk, are used as the starting point for the simulated scenes. The simulator's computer then calls up the pictures as needed to

Fig. 5-8. This simulation of close-formation flying shows the degree of realism already available for pilot training. (Courtesy Goodyear Aerospace)

make a coherent flight. The computer also changes the scale, orientation, and direction of the pictures to achieve continuous realism. To simulate moving objects such as other aircraft or missiles (as well as fill in gaps where photos are not available), computer-generated graphics could be inserted. And aerial-reconnaissance photos of targets behind enemy lines could be included so crews could practice before taking off on real missions.

One of the problems yet to be solved is how to reproduce scenes close to the ground from photos taken at altitude. For example, how do you simulate nap-of-the-Earth helicopter flights amongst trees and rocks using photos taken from above? Then there is the need to randomly access each videodisk frame within $\frac{1}{30}$ sec. while smoothly changing from one picture to the next to give a continuous moving scene.

A complete simulated view out of a cockpit requires many CRTs and racks of electronics. Costs can quickly get out of hand. This might be overcome, however, by projecting a high-resolution picture directly in front of the pilot, in whatever direction he is looking, with a lower-resolution picture covering the rest of the scene (the human eye only has high resolution in the center of its field of vision). The technique shares some of the technology used in the helmet-mounted displays.

Fig. 5-10. Lifelike combat scenarios inside a 20-foot diameter sphere provide realistic combat training without ever leaving the ground. (Courtesy Goodyear Aerospace)

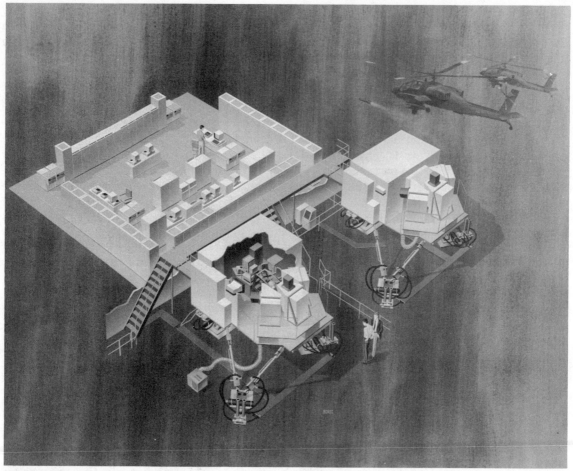

Fig. 5-11. Twin simulators like these could be used to train pilots of tandem-seat helicopters and fighters. (Courtesy Link Flight Simulation Division of the Singer Company)

Flying Simulators

In contrast to flight simulators, which remain on the ground, fly*ing* simulators do their job in the air. NASA uses three highly modified Grumman Aerospace *Gulfstream II* airplanes to train astronauts; the planes are called Shuttle Trainer Aircraft. The NT-33A, a Lockheed T-33 trainer updated with modern avionics, has been used to train F-16, F-17, and F-18 pilots. And an advanced cockpit had been grafted to the front end of a

Sikorsky S-76 helicopter to evaluate new technologies for the Army's new Light Scout/Attack and Utility Helicopter, the LHX (FIGS. 5-13 AND 5-14).

Flying simulators have a real advantage when testing out new, unproven ideas. If an idea does not work as expected and the flying simulator gets into trouble, the aircraft can quickly revert to its original safe form. In the future you will see more and more flying simulators used to cut both development and training costs.

Fig. 5-12. This Boeing 757 simulator is already used for training and maintaining proficiency of commercial airline pilots. (Courtesy Link Flight Simulation Division of the Singer Company)

Fig. 5-13. The NC-131H Total In-Flight Simulator can be used to simulate the subsonic handling of a wide variety of aircraft, ranging from supersonic transports and bombers to the Space Shuttle. (Courtesy Calspan Corporation, Buffalo, New York)

Fig. 5-14. Although the NT-33A's airframe is decades old, this flying simulator is used to investigate stability and control characteristics of future aircraft. (Courtesy Calspan Corporation, Buffalo, New York)

=6=

Materials and Manufacturing

N o MATTER how good an aerodynamic design or a propulsion concept might be, it is not of much use if materials are not available to transform it from a laboratory experiment to a practical reality. The history of aviation is filled with great ideas that had to wait until the right materials came along to make them work. The forward-swept wing and the scramjet are two examples that immediately come to mind.

The vocabulary of the aerospace world already includes such terms as composites, superalloys, ceramics, carbon-carbon, and metal-matrix composites. Many of these materials are already in use, however, advanced materials are just in their infancy. The realization of their full potential lies in the future.

Of equal importance to materials is the ability to manufacture the airframe, engine, and black boxes economically and in sufficient quantities. Manufacturing is entering its second major revolution. The first was the Industrial Revolution itself. The current revolution has produced automated and robotic factories that build items designed on a computer screen, not on a drawing board. Future aircraft will be developed with computer-aided design (CAD) techniques and will be built in highly automated aircraft and engine plants using computer-aided manufacturing (CAM). Both CAD and CAM are already in use in the aerospace industry, but only in rudimentary forms.

METALS

For decades aluminum has been the mainstay of the aerospace industry, and the suppliers of aluminum products are trying to keep it that way. Future aircraft, however, must be lighter to achieve improved fuel economy, and their higher speeds produce temperatures too high for conventional aluminum.

Aluminum Alloys

To see how new forms of aluminum will impact the aerospace industry in the 21st century, just measure how much aluminum is used in a typical commercial airliner. Today, over 70 percent of the aircraft is made of aluminum. By the year 2000, new lightweight aluminum alloys will comprise over 50 percent of the airliner.

One of the most promising aluminum alloys under development today is aluminum-lithium (FIG. 6-1). Aluminum-lithium is about 10 percent lighter and 10 percent stiffer than regular aluminum. If aluminum-lithium were substituted in current aircraft, overall weights could be reduced by about 8 to 10 percent, and newly designed aluminum-lithium aircraft could be as much as 15 percent lighter.

But there is more to aluminum-lithium than just light weight. Because of its superior resistance to fatigue, components made of aluminum-lithium will last two to three times longer. Also, parts can be fabricated with current machinery, alleviating the need for huge investments in new equipment and retraining of employees.

Aluminum-lithium alloys do have some disadvantages. For one thing, they are roughly two to three times more expensive than ordinary aluminum, due in part to the high cost of lithium, currently about $30 per pound. This means that lithium scrap must be salvaged, a manpower-intensive process. Also, because molten aluminum-lithium can explode upon contact with moisture during the casting process, stringent safety precautions must be observed. Even so, aluminum-lithium components will cost considerably less than parts made of plastic composites, at least on a per-pound basis.

Other aluminum alloys are being developed to operate at much higher temperatures, even up to the temperature regimes that now require use of titanium. Ordinary aluminum starts to lose its strength at 250-300° F. Experts believe they can make aluminum-based materials that can function at temperatures up to 650° F. These aluminum alloys could be about 15 percent lighter and as much as 65 percent cheaper than equivalent titanium parts.

Superalloys

High-temperature applications are the focus of superalloy research. Many advanced superalloys gain their characteristics by combining basic materials like titanium, aluminum, beryllium, nickel, cobalt, molybdenum, and niobium. Titanium-aluminide, one such superalloy, will increase the current operating range of titanium from 950° F to about 1500° F, but without an increase in weight. Another metallic material gaining popularity is beryllium, one of the lightest structural materials known. Beryllium has excellent heat-dissipating properties, making it a natural for such applications as braking systems on high-performance aircraft.

Production of Metallic Materials

Great strides will also be made in the way metallic materials are produced and formed into useful components. Time-honored metalworking processes such as forging, casting, extruding, and machining will take on new dimensions, and entirely new processes will be created.

One of the major new forms of metal processing is called rapid solidification. Here, molten metals are cooled at tremendously rapid rates, as high as one million degrees per second. The resulting materials are homogeneous because, there is not enough time for large grains to form. The small grains or crystals that do form are uniformly distributed. The end result is that rapidly solidified alloys are much stronger and have higher melting points. In addition, metals undergoing rapid solidification pass through "metastable" phases in which they have special properties that are just beginning to be understood by scientists.

Because of the potential of rapidly solidified alloys, many companies are looking at a wide variety of techniques to produce the finely powdered materials that are the end product of the process (FIG. 6-2). These powders are then usually pressed or extruded into ingots or billets or even the final part. One of the simplest procedures, called splat cooling, involves spraying hot, molten droplets onto a cold surface. A variation on this idea is to spray

Fig. 6-1. Opposite: Two aluminum-lithium panels being flight tested on the wings of an F-15. (Courtesy McDonnell Douglas)

Fig. 6-2. Here the fine powders of alloys are being formed by the rapid-solidification technique. After being sprayed out in molten form, the alloys are cooled very, very rapidly. (Courtesy Pratt & Whitney)

the fine droplets into an extremely cold, inert-gas environment. Another idea is to pour the molten material onto a rapidly spinning wheel which, through centrifugal action, breaks up the material into fine droplets and throws them into a cold-gas atmosphere for rapid cooling.

The powders can be formed into useful shapes in several ways. For example, the powders can be heated and then forced under high pressure through a small hole, much like toothpaste out of a tube, to form extruded billets. These billets can then be machined into the desired parts. In the dynamic-compaction technique the powder is placed in a die shaped like the final component. The powdered ma-

terial is compacted using a gun barrel and a projectile. The projectile is "fired" down the barrel by ultrahigh gas pressure, or even by explosives, and the gas in front of the projectile compacts the powder in the die. This process is also known as net-shaping, because the final part produced needs no further machining.

Rapid solidification can also be used to put high-temperature and high-strength coatings on components such as parts of gas-turbine engines. One technique is to use a plasma flame to heat the surface of the part. The part is then rapidly cooled to retain the desired characteristics in the thin coating.

Another process, called laser glazing, uses a high-powered laser to heat the part, forming a thin layer of molten material on the surface. The actual cooling is done to the bulk of the part by heat conduction at rates as high as 10 million degrees-per-second. Laser glazing has the advantage of only affecting the surface; the material below retains its original properties. Also, by applying many layers, rather complex parts can be made.

One technique that has been around for a while, but shows great promise for the future, is called superplastic forming. Here the metal, in putty-like form, is worked vigorously to obtain the optimum grain structure. The material is then formed into the desired shape before it is heat-treated, rapidly cooled, and aged (FIG. 6-3).

In another technique, called diffusion bonding, parts are joined together under very high pressures and temperatures. As the name implies, joining occurs because the atoms of the parts being mated actually flow, or diffuse, across the solid boundary. Unlike welding, the materials being joined do not melt.

COMPOSITES

Like the transistor, microchip, and laser, composite materials are one of the great technological advances of the last half of the 20th century and will play a major role in making future aircraft designs possible (FIGS 6-4 AND 6-5).

Any material that is made of two separate and quite different components is given the generic name "composite." The components are the "fibers" that normally give the composite its strength and the "matrix" that holds the fibers together. The matrix also provides the composite material with other desired properties, such as resistance to high temperature, stiffness, or immunity to corrosion.

The fiber part of the composite can be of such materials as boron, silicon carbide, or aramid, and can range in size from small particles to long, continuous threads. While particles and short fibers are randomly dispersed in the matrix material, long fibers can be woven, knitted, or braided into the final shape of the component and then embedded in the matrix material to obtain the desired characteristics.

Although the matrix material is most usually thought of as some type of plastic, a new technology called metal-matrix composites (MMCs) is emerging. Here, fibers made of such materials as silicon carbide, boron carbide, and graphite are combined with a metal matrix made of aluminum or magnesium. Again, the fibers can range anywhere in size from small particles to continuous filaments. The resulting MMC is stronger, stiffer, and lighter than the pure aluminum or magnesium, and its other properties, such as thermal conductivity, are enhanced.

What makes composite materials so attractive is that the composite designer can blend the fibers and matrix into a new material with new and better properties than those of the individual constituent materials. For example, fragile glass, when spun into fine fiber, has six times the tensile strength of ordinary steel. But full advantage of this extraordinary strength can be taken only if the glass fibers are embedded in a plastic-type material that is ductile. This allows the composite to be formed into a finished component that can be subjected to bending and twisting stresses (FIG. 6-6).

The use of composites essentially allows the engineers to reverse the design process. In the past, they had to design around available materials. Now, they can specifically design the composite materials to meet the needs of the job.

The earliest, and most commonly used composite, is fiberglass, made by imbedding glass in a matrix of "thermosetting" plastic.*

Although fiberglass was widely used as early as the 1950s for boats and automobiles (e.g., the Chevrolet *Corvette*), uses in the aircraft industry came somewhat slower. The Boeing 707, the first

---

*Thermosetting plastics cannot be remelted after they have cooled in the forming process. By contrast, "thermoplastics" can be reheated and reformed over and over again. Thermoplastic materials are of great interest today because they are recyclable, and this interest will grow as resources become scarcer. New industries will spring up to recycle everything from thermoplastic beverage bottles to thermoplastic automobile bodies, and the need for dumps will decline.

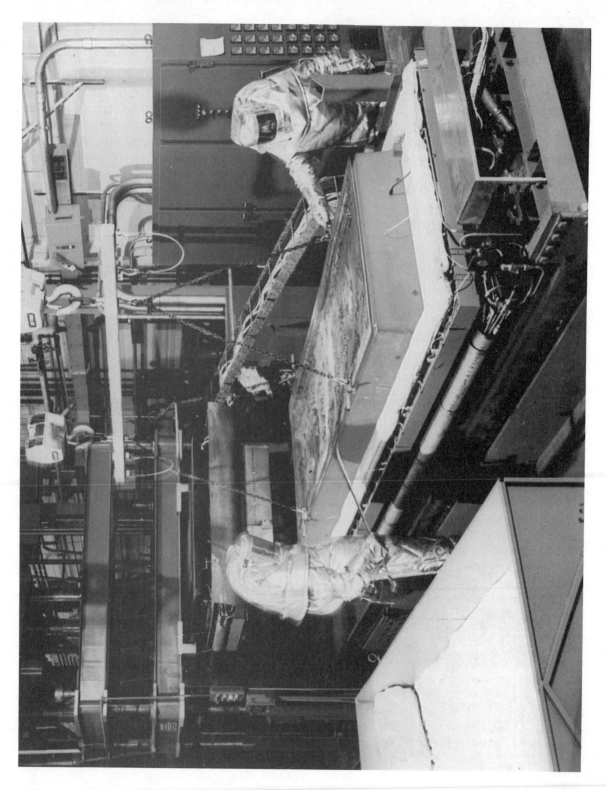

Fig. 6-3. Opposite: Titanium parts being made by superplastic forming. Insulated suits are needed by the handlers because temperatures are as high as 1700° F. (Courtesy LTV)

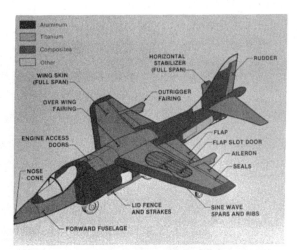

airliner to use composites, was only about two percent fiberglass. But the aircraft industry soon saw the advantages of these man-made materials, and the Boeing 747 was almost 30 percent fiberglass. Boeing's new 757 and 767 airliners also have about 30 percent of their structures made of composites—but of more sophisticated materials like graphite-epoxy and graphite-Kevlar hybrids. Predictions are that as much as 65 percent of the 21st-century airliner will be made of advanced composites.

Military uses are equally impressive. Fifty percent of the Advanced Tactical Fighter will probably be made of composites; that's about twice the composite material content of any military aircraft flying today.

Although composites are made from petroleum-based chemicals, their petroleum usage is very small compared to total petroleum usage. They also represent a very efficient use of the petroleum and result in high-priced items, meaning large payoffs for the resources invested. The composite industry would probably be the last to be drastically affected by future petroleum shortages.

Much more materials research is underway in university, government, and industrial laboratories today that will make the aircraft of the 21st century possible. But, it takes a long time, sometimes as much as 15 or 20 years, from the time a new ma-

Fig. 6-4. The AV-8B *Harrier* was the first high-performance military aircraft to use composite material extensively. (Courtesy McDonnell Douglas)

terial or process is "invented" until it is actually used on a production aircraft. During this interim time, extensive testing is required to fully understand its properties, and fabrication techniques have to be perfected to allow economical manufacture.

FACTORIES OF THE FUTURE

A revolution is already underway in the way aircraft are designed and built, with the main objective being to reduce the spiraling costs of new aircraft. Technologies like the high-speed computer, robotics, artificial intelligence, and machine vision are the keystones of this revolution.

Fig. 6-5. The Goodyear Blimp-of-the-Future, the GZ-22, will make extensive use of composites, especially in the gondola. (Courtesy Goodyear Aerospace)

Fig. 6-6. The composite structure of a lightplane being formed in a special mold. (Courtesy Marquardt & Roche)

In the aerospace industry, most labor costs result not from the people who do the hands-on work in building aircraft but from the people who charge their time to overhead. These include the tiers of managers, supervisors, schedulers, quality control experts, and a myriad of other paper shufflers currently needed to keep the aircraft production line going. Because of the complexity of new aerospace systems, the demands of the customer (often the bureaucratic government), and the low production rates for most systems, overhead dominates the total cost of a new airplane. Depending on the aircraft, overhead costs today can account for up to 70 percent of the total price of an airplane.

Fortunately, the computer does its best work on exactly these overhead tasks. Computers will take over many of the tasks done by roomfuls of people, including filing and retrieving data, scheduling material and machine use, making design changes, and monitoring the quality of the product.

Today, there is great interest in computer-integrated manufacturing (CIM), which integrates the fairly developed concepts of CAD, CAM, and CAE (computer-aided engineering).

CAD replaces the traditional drafting board for the design engineer (FIG. 6-7). The designing of an aircraft part or even an entire airplane is done on a computer screen. CAD has progressed to the point where the designer can see the work in multicolors and rotate it to any position. Changes to the design can be made via keyboard or light pen. When the designer is satisfied with his work, he

Fig. 6-7. An engineer using computer-aided design (CAD). After he is done, his design will be interfaced with computer-aided manufacturing (CAM) to produce the component. (Courtesy Boeing)

gives the system a command to print his drawings so they can be sent to the factory. Better yet, they can be converted to computer instructions that are read directly by the machines of a CAM system, machines that might cut metal or paint parts. In the CIM triad, computers and software do the multitude of engineering calculations to ensure that a part or an entire airplane will do its job over its intended life. Included in this CAE concept are engineering analyses that range from aerodynamic and thermodynamic calculations to stress and fatigue computations.

The three component systems of CIM will have to talk to one another using common computer languages and common nomenclature. Artificial intelligence will undoubtedly play a key role in the CIM system; expert systems will weigh alternatives and automatically make logical choices.

CIM offers many advantages, including ease of redesign. This is very important in the aerospace industry where parts and aircraft are made in relatively small quantities. While it might take a machinist hours to set up his milling machine or lathe to make just one new part, a single CAM machine can be reprogrammed very rapidly to make a multitude of different parts.

CIM would not only instruct the CAM machines to make the part, but also instruct material handling equipment to get the raw material from the storage bin and route it through the entire manufacturing process. The material handling aspect is a very important part of the increasingly favored "just-in-time" inventory philosophy, in which only enough inventory is maintained to keep production going and materials are delivered to work stations only as needed. While the concept reduces inventory costs and facilities tremendously, it does require very sophisticated computer control.

Quality control is another area that will see tremendous automation. In the future, parts will not have to be inspected by humans. Sensors located within machines, in furnaces, and on assembly lines will immediately sense when things are not perfect. Computers, using artificial-intelligence techniques, will not only stop production, but will analyze the situation and make the necessary corrections. Inspection techniques will rely heavily on machine-vision technology to "look at" objects and digitize what is "seen" into the language a computer can understand. Other fault-sensing techniques will use ultrasonics, infrared sensors, and lasers.

Naturally, robots will populate the automated aircraft factories of the future (PLATE 12). Because they are not subject to the human frailties of boredom, fatigue, or an "off day," robots can be programmed to unerringly produce parts to exact specifications. They also work well in toxic or hazardous environments.

Although automated aircraft manufacturing will require fewer people, the human element will still be the most important ingredient. People will, however, be removed from the tedious jobs. Instead, they will be required to write the software, design the programs and processes, monitor the overall system, be the "experts" for the artificial intelligence systems, and finally, maintain and repair all the sophisticated equipment.

Automated equipment will not only be found in factories producing new aircraft, but also in facilities that are "recycling" old aircraft to update them with the latest technology. Development is already underway on automated equipment that can strip paint, remove rivets, and duplicate new parts from the old parts themselves (when the original engineering drawings are no longer available). As stated earlier, there will be intense interest in modernizing the aircraft in use today so they can perform first-line service well into the 21st century.

7

Military Aircraft

THE 21ST CENTURY will see a few completely new aircraft designs interspersed among many familiar airplanes that are flying today with the military services. Only when current systems, or modified and updated versions of current aircraft, can no longer do the job will scarce national resources be committed to the development of entirely new systems. For example, the Soviets' advancing threat and their ability to counter the American threat will definitely be a reason to develop new systems.

Because of the long lead time between design conception and actual fielding in an operational unit (today this can take as long as a decade or more), the designs now in the planning stages will be the mainline systems of the next century, that is, if they can pass the myriad of approvals and do not get cancelled along the way.

Every major new military system represents a significant portion of the national defense budget, so there will be absolutely no room for "white elephants" in future military inventories. Unfor-

tunately, this environment could produce conservative designs; the military and the manufacturers may shy away from promising technologies that have even the slightest tinge of risk. Technologies will have to be well proven before they are incorporated in a new design.

NATIONAL AEROSPACE PLANE

In his 1986 State of the Union address, President Reagan officially announced, "We are going forward with research on a new Orient Express that could, by the end of the next decade, take off from Dulles Airport, accelerate up to 25 times the speed of sound attaining low earth orbit, or fly to Tokyo within two hours."

In October 1987, McDonnell Douglas, General Dynamics, and Rockwell International were awarded contracts to begin design of a National Aerospace Plane (NASP). (FIGS. 7-1 AND 7-2).

Serious investigations of hypersonic aerospace vehicles have been around since the early 1960s.

105

However, the technology was not mature enough to make any of the concepts economically feasible, nor were the missions for such a vehicle clearly defined. Instead, the U.S. went ahead with the Space Shuttle and its rocket propulsion system, which were considered more feasible and appropriate to support our military and civilian space programs.

In recent times, there has appeared a renewed interest in an aerospace vehicle that could reduce the cost of putting payloads into orbit as well as carrying passengers at hypersonic speeds. Coupled to this are several major breakthroughs in propulsion, materials, and computers that could not only make such an aircraft feasible, but economically practical.

One of the reasons for developing the NASP is to gain a replacement for the Space Shuttle. The goal is a space launcher that could place payloads in orbit at greatly reduced costs and with significantly reduced turnaround times between launches (FIG. 7-3). The NASP would take off and land horizontally from airports designed for regular large jet aircraft. There would be no need for launch pads, recovery facilities, vertical-assembly buildings, and huge numbers of support personnel.

A major potential user of any future space shuttle is the Strategic Defense Initiative (SDI) or "Star Wars" program. Most of the SDI concepts under consideration will be based in space and will require many, many launches to get them into orbit.

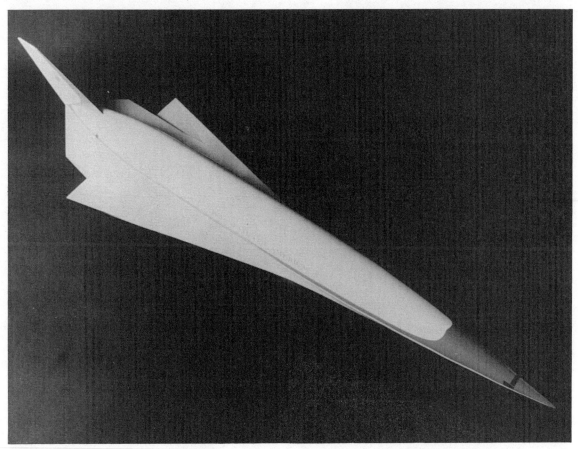

Fig. 7-2. The technology for the NASP could be used in a variety of hypersonic vehicles ranging from a space shuttle to transoceanic airliners. (Courtesy NASA)

Other versions of the NASP could perform reconnaissance, filling gaps in satellite coverage caused by weather obscuration, the physical laws of orbital mechanics, or loss due to enemy action. The NASP could be a logical replacement for the SR-71, which will be almost 40 years old by the turn of the century. An interceptor version could be fired from great distances at enemy threats including low-flying bombers and cruise missiles. The Navy is interested in such an aircraft for enhanced fleet protection from bases right in the U.S. With its ability to be recalled and its ultrahigh speed, it could even replace both the manned bomber and ICBM in the Triad concept of strategic deterrence.

A very significant step in the NASP program is a subscale prototype. The X-30A, as this technology demonstrator most likely will be called, will be able to fly at speeds of over Mach 8; it should be flying by the early to mid-1990s. Actual NASPs could be in operation around the year 2000.

Propulsion is the key technology for a successful NASP. A hydrogen-fueled scramjet is currently the most viable engine for the NASP. By using a composite engine, the plane can be accelerated from the ramp to hypersonic speeds of Mach 17 or even Mach 25.

One critical mechanical consideration is the landing and takeoff system. With a loaded weight of as much as 1½ million pounds, the stress of takeoff makes for challenging landing gear designs. One idea is to use a sled-like trolley (FIG. 7-4 AND PLATE 9).

We now have the technology to build a fleet of NASPs, and the military and space programs have definite requirements that could take advantage of hypersonic aircraft. What remains to be seen is if the national budget can handle the enormous cost of developing and acquiring a NASP fleet.

ADVANCED TACTICAL FIGHTER

The Advanced Tactical Fighter (ATF), designed to eventually replace the McDonnell Douglas F-15, will see initial operational duty in the mid-1990s and will be the U.S. Air Force's main-line air-superiority fighter well into the 21st century (FIG. 7-5). The Navy might also use a version of the ATF (or at least much of the ATF's technology) in what it calls the ATA, or Advanced Tactical Aircraft.

The need for a new fighter stems from the rapid pace the Soviets are making in fighter technology and in systems that can detect and negate our fighters. In 1984 alone, the Soviets fielded two new first-class fighters, the SU-27 and MiG-29. And these are not crude and simplistic machines; they, too, incorporate high technology to narrow the gap between Soviet capabilities and American F-14s, F-15s, F-16s and F-18s. Not only do the Soviets' fighters have performance equivalent to America's, but capabilities in such things as look-down/shoot-down radars and weapon range and accuracy are roughly as good. On the ground, their radars and anti-aircraft weapons continue to improve. Add to this the higher Soviet production rate—they outproduce America by more than 2-to-1—and you see why a new U.S. fighter is warranted.

Although updating the F-15 was (and still is) a possibility if costs get out of hand, the Air Force was convinced that the design of the ATF had to start with a blank computer screen. For starters, by the time the ATF becomes operational, the F-15's technology will be about two decades old (FIG. 7-6). And while it would be possible to cram much of the new technology into the F-15, the important characteristics of the F-15, such as its efficiency, maneuverability, and radar and IR signatures, cannot be altered much. What is needed is an entirely new aircraft with new basic capabilities, such as non-afterburning supersonic cruise, short-field takeoff and landing capability, and low

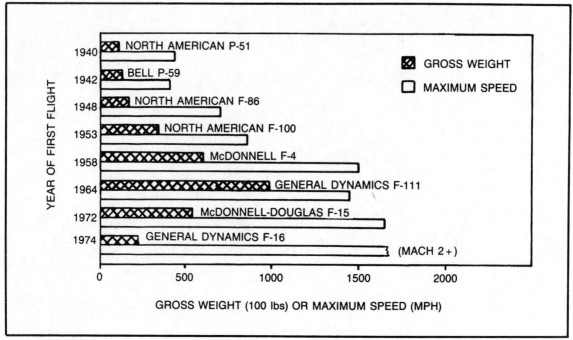

Fig. 7-6. U.S. fighters have become lighter and faster.

observables (PLATE 1). However, the Air Force planners have to be sure that the ATF does not go overboard by incorporating such overly advanced technology that it would be difficult to maintain. The ATF will represent a compromise between the F-15 and a "Star Wars" fighter.

The ATF is still in the very preliminary stages. Although the use of a particular technology will depend on the final design of the aircraft and whether or not the technology is technically, operationally, and economically feasible, it is possible to speculate on the final design.

For efficient operation over a flight regime ranging from cruise to combat, variable geometry (or even the mission-adaptive wing) could be used. Because supermaneuverability is so important for the future, control surfaces could be significantly altered, such as replacing the horizontal tail with forward canards. Supermaneuverability in the ATF could mean a 50 percent increase in supersonic turn rate and a 25 percent increase in the turn rate at subsonic speeds. A highly blended body would improve aerodynamic efficiency during sustained

flight at supersonic speeds, leading to important gains in combat radius—up to four times that of the F-15.

As much as 50 percent of the airframe and wings could be made of advanced composites, including thermoplastics and radar-absorbing materials to make the ATF "stealthy" (FIGS. 7-7 AND 7-8). Advanced metallics such as lithium-aluminum would be used in its structure. The end result would be a 20-percent-lighter aircraft compared to one designed using technology of the F-15 era.

Advanced avionics are an important part of the ATF story and represent about 40 percent of the total aircraft development cost. The flight-control system will be digital fly-by-wire (possibly flight-by-light if the technology matures fast enough).

With a digital flight-control system (DFCS), the pilot essentially only needs to command the aircraft to perform maneuvers. The DFCS does the fine-tuning and performs the maneuver by efficiently

Fig. 7-7. Opposite: The ATF's aerodynamic shape will be governed by its need to be "stealthy". (Courtesy Westinghouse)

moving control surfaces as many as 40 times a second. This "smart" DFCS computer can even be programmed to ensure that maneuvers do not exceed any of the aircraft's structural limits; the pilot will not be able to rip the wings off the aircraft while pulling out of a dive or break the fuselage in half by turning too sharply.

The ATF cockpit has been dubbed an "all-glass" cockpit because CRTs will replace most of the dials and gauges. There may even be one continuous flat-panel display. The pilot might be able to call up the information he needs simply by touching the screen or uttering a voice command. Not only could the pilot talk to his airplane, but it could talk to him, giving him aural warnings and instructions by a computer-generated voice. On the screen, the pilot could observe the position of ground forces and enemy aircraft while at the same time monitoring vital aircraft parameters. A "God's-eye view" could allow him to see the whole situation from a vantage point above and behind his aircraft, sort of a video-game view of the combat arena—except this game is for real. Of course, there will be an advanced HUD that might even be coupled to a helmet-mounted visor display that would let the pilot focus his attention outside the cockpit. Artificial intelligence in the form of the "Pilot Associate" would ease his workload by helping make decisions and selecting weapons, from missiles for long-range targets to guns for high-G dogfights.

These advanced avionics place tremendous demands on onboard computers; VHSIC computer technology will be needed to shrink the size and weight of the aircraft's electronics and provide faster computation and greater reliability. To help guarantee mission success and the ability to return home safely, the ATF's avionics could troubleshoot themselves and configure themselves to bypass failed components or even those damaged in battle (FIG. 7-9).

The pilot's comfort will not be forgotten. A closed-loop environmental control system could integrate both life-support and life-protection func-tions. This would include everything from heat, air conditioning, oxygen, and cabin pressure to protection against chemical, nuclear, and biological threats as well as safeguards against laser damage to the pilot's eyes.

Because of the high G's encountered, possibly higher than in any other fighter to date, the ATF pilot will sit in an inclined seat like that in the F-16. For forces up to 9 G's his G-suit will inflate instantaneously and automatically, squeezing his body to keep him from passing out.

The ATF's engine is expected to provide up to twice as much thrust per pound of engine weight as current fighter engines at supersonic speeds, and 20 to 30 percent more thrust at subsonic speeds without burning more fuel—and perhaps burning less. The engine would also provide 75 percent of its thrust without afterburning, so the ATF could cruise at speeds of about Mach 1.2 with a greatly reduced infrared signature. The planned engine will have up to 40 percent fewer parts, meaning lower cost, greater reliability, and reduced maintenance. Advanced materials such as ceramics will allow it to operate at turbine inlet temperatures about 500 degrees higher than previous engines. The engines may be equipped with rectangular, two-dimensional nozzles with thrust-vectoring and reversing features to enhance maneuverability and provide a measure of STOL capability. Both General Electric and Pratt & Whitney are working on low-bypass, afterburning turbofans to meet these goals.

The ATF program shows how massive and costly the development of a new military aircraft really is. Even though just about all the major aerospace companies—Boeing, Grumman, General Dynamics, Lockheed, McDonnell Douglas, Northrop, and Rockwell—did conceptual studies of the ATF as early as 1983, the first ATF prototypes will probably not fly until the 1989-1990 time period. Because of the magnitude of the effort and the resources required, two teams of contractors have been chosen to build two prototypes. One team consists of Lockheed-California assisted by Boeing and General Dynamics. The other includes Northrop and McDonnell Douglas. These prototypes have been designated the YF-22 and YF-23, and one will

eventually be chosen to go into production. Today, each ATF is expected to cost $35-40 million, and the whole program represents an investment of $35 billion. Currently, 750 airplanes are planned.

The ATF is not the only new fighter under development. As mentioned previously, the Navy has its ATA program. Saab is working on its multi-role *Gripen* that will meet Sweden's, and perhaps other countries', needs for a interceptor, reconnaissance, and air-attack fighter well into the 21st century. In France, Avions Marcel Dassault-Breguet Aviation is developing an advanced-technology, Mach 2+ fighter called the *Rafale* (FIG. 7-10). Across the channel, British Aerospace is demonstrating the technology for a future multinational *Eurofighter* (FIG. 7-11).

What about the fighters that might come after the ones currently being developed? Well, they will incorporate those technologies that promise other performance and operational improvements, but were not quite ready for aircraft like the ATF. They will also include ideas that either are still in embryonic stages in research laboratories or have not been thought of yet (FIG. 7-12 AND PLATES 4 AND 7).

Decades from now, the fighter will be a "plastic" airplane with extensive use of composites including carbon-carbon, metal-matrix, and ceramic varieties. The empty weight of these fighters could be cut in half, affecting payload and range capabilities. Composites could keep the aircraft intact and "cool" even when flying at Mach 3+ for sustained periods. The "smart" skins would also serve as antennas and sensors, further reducing weight and eliminating drag-producing empennages.

The cockpits of 21st century fighters will use the results of expanding computer and electronics technology. If pilots think the HUD and HMD are great, wait until they see the three-dimensional spherical display that could replace them. This wraparound display is so advanced that engineers are not sure how they would make it work, but they want it because of the flexibility it offers, as well as the vast amount of information that can be presented in easy-to-understand form. Of course, artificial intelligence will have progressed far beyond the Pilot Associate systems used in aircraft like the ATF.

Other features of the fighter will include active flight controls that will allow the fighter to fly through severe weather and violent maneuvering with minimum damage to the airframe. Self-repairing flight controls will be able to reconfigure an aircraft to continue to fly and fight, even if it loses control surfaces such as its elevons or rudder.

The flight-control system could even sense when the pilot is unconscious because of combat injuries or a G-induced blackout. One technique for determining consciousness is to monitor the pilot's blinking. (When a person blacks out, his eyes do not automatically blink, and just before unconsciousness his gaze is fixed.) This might be combined with other monitoring techniques like watching for the drooping of the pilot's head, absence of a firm grip on the controls, or the loss of blood pressure pulse in the brain. Much research is currently underway to reduce the chance of the pilot blacking out in the supermaneuverable fighters of the future. Solutions could include more sophisticated G-suits and even special drugs.

For propulsion, these advanced fighters could have engines with 1,000-2,000 parts, compared with the 15,000-20,000 parts used today. This drastic reduction could be achieved with advanced materials and manufacturing techniques that allow complex parts to be produced as a single unit with a minimum of machining and finishing. Weights will also go down so that engines will routinely achieve 20-to-1 thrust-to-weight ratios.

THE STEALTH FIGHTER AND BOMBER

The U.S. Air Force has not released much information on "low observables," the Stealth fighter or the Stealth bomber (the Advanced Technology Bomber—ATB). However, this is as it should be

Fig. 7-10. (Page 118) A French fighter of the future, the *Rafale*. (Courtesy Avions Marcel Dassault - Breguet Aviation)

Fig. 7-11. (Page 119) This is the *Eurofighter*, a European concept for an advanced fighter. (Courtesy British Aerospace)

Plate 1. An artist's concept of an Advanced Tactical Fighter showing the emphasis on stealth characteristics. (Courtesy Lockheed-California)

Plate 2. An artist's concept of the F-19 Stealth fighter. (Copyright 1987 R.A. Sweeney)

Plate 3. This 21st-century fighter concept uses thrust-vectoring nozzles for enhanced maneuvering at transonic speeds. (Courtesy Boeing)

Plate 4. A concept for a long range, supersonic cruise and maneuver fighter. (Courtesy Boeing)

Plate 5. One potential use of the V-22 *Osprey* is for search and rescue missions. (Courtesy Bell Helicopters Textron)

Plate 6. A military aircraft based on the X-wing concept. (Courtesy Sikorsky Aircraft)

Plate 7. A Boeing concept for a future supersonic fighter. (Courtesy Boeing)

Marshall Osborne

Plate 8. A rather advanced helicopter concept that includes laser target seekers/designators and stealth characteristics. (Courtesy Boeing Vertol)

Plate 9. This concept would use a powered trolley to launch the National Aerospace Plane. The trolley would be dropped after takeoff. (Courtesy Rockwell International)

Plate 10. By using an air-cushion landing system, future aircraft will be able to operate from battle-damaged runways. (Courtesy U.S. Air Force)

Plate 11. The HOTOL, a British hypersonic aircraft concept. (Courtesy British Aerospace)

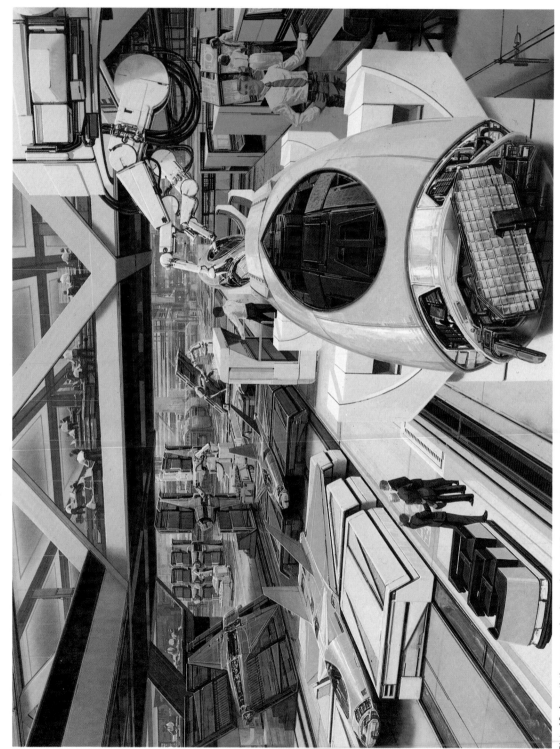

Plate 12. An artist's concept of a future Advanced Tactical Fighter assembly line. (Courtesy Lockheed California, art by Syd Mead)

Plate 13. A cargo aircraft using the joined-wing concept. (Courtesy Lockheed Georgia)

Plate 14. One of several scissor-wing airliner concepts. In this case, twin fuselages would be used in conjunction with the pivoting oblique wing. (Courtesy NASA)

Plate 15. One advantage of a dual-body cargo carrier is much faster loading and unloading ability. (Courtesy NASA)

Plate 16. A mockup of the Airbus A320 cockpit, the first of the airliner cockpits of the future. (Courtesy Airbus Industrie)

Plate 17. A commuter airliner with propfans installed. (Courtesy Lockheed Georgia)

Plate 18. The ultimate business jet, a supersonic version from British Aerospace. (Courtesy British Aerospace)

Plate 19. The Rotec *Panther Plus*, an airplane that's just for fun. (Courtesy Rotec)

Plate 20. Satellite systems like GPS Navstar will be able to communicate directly with military, commercial, and general-aviation aircraft. (Courtesy Rockwell International Satellite Systems Division)

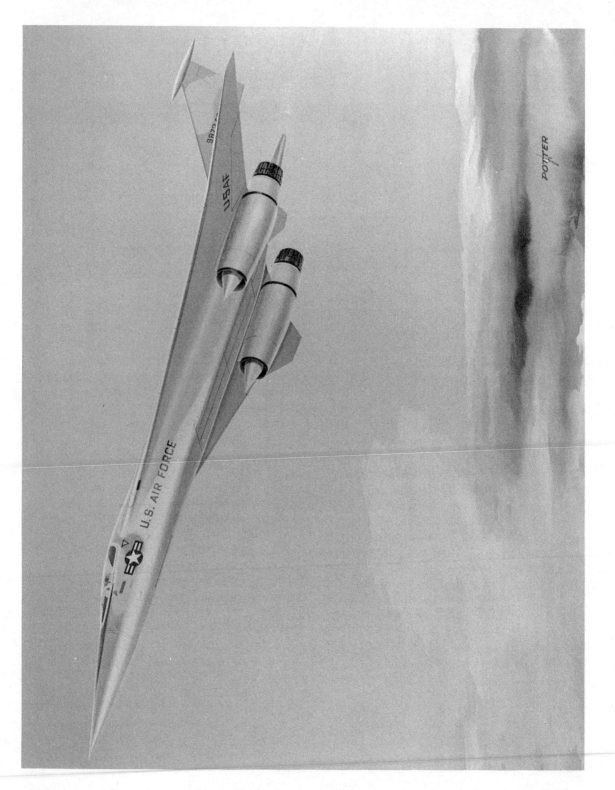

because the idea behind these two aircraft is the ability to penetrate enemy defenses undetected. It is important, therefore, not to give away aircraft characteristics beforehand.

The need for Stealth aircraft was driven by improved Soviet air defense capabilities, starting with the surface-to-air missiles that were able to shoot down Gary Powers' U-2. This led to the obsolescence of the Convair B-58 and the cancellation of the trisonic North American B-70, both of which were designed for high-altitude penetration. Instead, the venerable B-52 was extensively modified with new electronic warfare equipment and air-launched missiles to help during penetration. Most importantly, tactics and equipment were developed for aircraft like the B-52, F-100 and F-105 so they could fly beneath Soviet detection radar.

Originally, the North American B-1 bomber was designed to fly at Mach 2 and high altitudes even though the primary mission was low-level penetration. Later, in what was announced as an economy move, the Mach 2 requirement was dropped. When President Reagan reinstated the B-1 program (now called B-1B) after it had been canceled by the Carter administration, the bomber was designed to fly no faster than just above the speed of sound with low-level penetration at speeds of about 600 MPH (FIG. 7-13). The B-1B also received dramatic improvements in low-observable characteristics and on-board defensive electronics all aimed at increasing its ability to penetrate enemy defenses.

In recent years, the Soviets have made great strides in their ability to counter our low-level attack characteristics, including advanced fighters with look-down, shoot-down radars. These put in jeopardy any low-level penetration system—whether it be a bomber, fighter, or Cruise missile—if it is based on old, "pre-stealth" technology. Therefore, there is great interest in advancing stealth technology rapidly. As an example, stealth capability has become a key requirement for the ATF. The Navy is considering a replacement for the F-14 which will probably have stealth characteristics. Also, a stealth-intensive advanced cruise missile has been flight tested.

The media have speculated about the Stealth fighter, supposedly called the F-19 and built by Lockheed (PLATE 2). Rumors of the existence of such a plane first surfaced when the military skipped from the F-18 to the F-20 in designating aircraft. The aviation magazines have described the

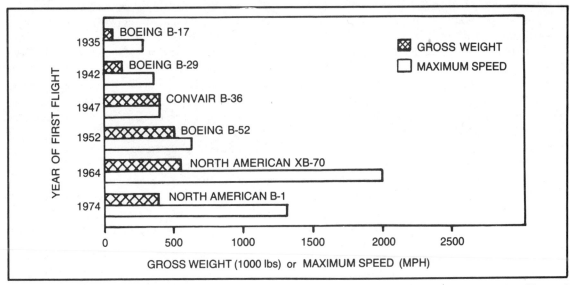

Fig. 7-13. Like fighters, bomber speeds and weights have increased, but with the B-1 this trend is reversing. Size and speed are no longer the key requirements for bombers.

F-19 as an experimental aircraft using the latest in electronic technology, materials, and aerodynamics to foil enemy radars and infrared sensors.

Aviation journalists believe that development of a Stealth fighter began about 1974 and that the first prototype flew in 1977. Furthermore, it is thought that a number of F-19s have been built and are being tested at a secret Nevada site. Speculation increased when a super-secret aircraft, conjectured to be the F-19, crashed in 1986 and the whole incident was put under tight security wraps.

The most sensitive parts of the Stealth fighter appear to be the aerodynamic shape and the materials used. To reduce radar signatures, advanced composites and special paints, such as on the SR-71, are supposedly incorporated, and special skin-fastening techniques are used. Fewer than 100 F-19s are expected to be built.

The existence of an ATB (Stealth bomber) is public knowledge, but its characteristics are still top secret. The Pentagon has acknowledged that stealth technology is being used by Northrop in developing a new "invisible" bomber, and there have been congressional debates over the advantages and disadvantages of the ATB versus the B-1B. The proponents of the ATB assert that the performance and survivability attributes of the ATB justify its slightly higher cost. The military is planning on approximately 130 ATBs with the first operational aircraft available as early as 1992.

Information available in the media leads to speculation that the ATB combines several technologies to gain its "invisibility" (its radar profile is said to be like that of a small bird). These could include a flying-wing shape with contours that minimize radar reflectivity. Further radar cross-section reduction comes from materials and coatings that are supposed to absorb radar energy rather than reflect it. The jet engines, which normally would be large radar reflectors and sources of IR energy, are shrouded and submerged in the fuselage. Though not completely invisible to the Soviet's powerful surveillance radars, the ATB is designed to thwart the type of pinpoint-guidance radars used to track aircraft for engagement by missiles or interceptor aircraft.

The issue of whether Stealth aircraft will use low-penetration, nap-of-the-Earth, or high-altitude tactics has been debated. In all probability, a fleet of stealthy aircraft—the ATF, ATB, and F-19—will use the whole flight envelope.

Because so little is publicly known about Stealth aircraft already flying, or about to fly, it is even harder to speculate about low-observable aircraft of the more distant future. Military history, however, tells us that for every technology breakthrough there is always a counter-breakthrough, so the search for even greater invisibility will go on, and the technology challenges will become ever more difficult.

V/STOL AIRCRAFT

For almost as long as man has wanted to fly he has also desired to take off and land just like a bird. This ability was finally achieved with the first successful helicopter flights in the 1940s. As useful as they have become, helicopters are however limited in their maximum forward speed (about 200 knots) and their range. So there have been many attempts to develop other types of Vertical/Short Takeoff and Landing (V/STOL) aircraft. But the field has been littered with more failures than successes. Like so many other mechanical things that are called upon to do multiple tasks, most V/STOL designs were not able to do every task very well. They also turned out to be quite complex in terms of both hardware and the skill needed to fly them. Also because of complexity, the basic craft turned out to be quite heavy, leaving little capacity for useful payloads. Because of the military potential of V/STOLs, however, a rather intense development effort has continued, and this investment in resources is starting to pay dividends.

V/STOL Fighter. The V/STOL fighter is especially attractive for close-support missions (FIG. 7-14). Instead of having to loiter in the air, expending fuel and exposed to enemy fire while waiting to be called for fire support, it can wait on the

Fig. 7-14. Opposite: This advanced V/STOL fighter would use plenum-chamber burning and thrust-vectoring nozzles to achieve supersonic speeds. (Courtesy McDonnell Douglas)

KENNETH W. KOTIK

ground at primitive air bases close to the battle zone. Because it can operate close to the battlefield, long flyback distances are not required, making high sortie rates possible. V/STOL fighters are of particular interest now because military planners know they must be able to operate from bomb-cratered runways right from the start in any future conflict. Likewise, the Navy likes the V/STOL fighter since it can operate from much smaller ships than giant aircraft carriers (FIG. 7-15). There can be more of them and they can be dispersed for better survivability. Because of its ability to fly slow and hover, the V/STOL fighter could provide a unique capability in urban-type warfare such as destroying sniper nests located in the upper stories of buildings (FIG. 7-16).

Aircraft that combine the best features of the

Fig. 7-15. With V/STOL aircraft, small ships like this could replace giant aircraft carriers. (Courtesy General Dynamics)

fixed-wing airplane and the helicopter fall into two categories: aircraft designed primarily for high-performance flight that can also take off and land vertically as well as hover (e.g., the *Harrier*), and aircraft that are basically fast helicopters. The Bell

Fig. 7-16. The ultimate fighter? This one would use composites extensively and have V/STOL capability. (Courtesy Phalanx Group)

124

tilt-rotor concept is one of the more successful aircraft in the latter category.

One of the disadvantages of the AV-8B *Harrier* is that it is not capable of supersonic speeds. Fortunately, developing a supersonic V/STOL is technically feasible, the most significant problem being the development of engines with sufficient thrust to accelerate the aircraft beyond Mach 1 and still be able to provide vertical lift. Because of the success and versatility of vectored thrust as used in the *Harrier*, the major engine manufacturers such as Rolls-Royce, General Electric, and Pratt & Whitney are working on engines that could power a supersonic V/STOL. The interest in these developments has been piqued because of the supermaneuverability it could provide future fighters, in addition to V/STOL capability.

The ability to take off vertically represents a large weight penalty in the V/STOL fighter. A modified version of the concept, the Short Take off and Vertical Landing (STOVL) aircraft would use a short rolling takeoff, perhaps assisted by such devices as a "ski-jump" launching pad. After its mission is completed, with its fuel and ordnance expended, it would return for a vertical landing. Just how dramatic the increase in payload can be by using a short rolling takeoff is demonstrated by the *Harrier*. If a 1200-foot ground roll is used, as opposed to a vertical takeoff, the maximum gross weight of the *Harrier* increases by about 50 percent, and most of this extra capacity can be used for fuel and ordnance.

Tilt-Rotor V/STOL. A military tilt-rotor V/STOL, the V-22 *Osprey,* being developed by Bell Helicopters Textron and Boeing Vertol, could finally become a reality in the 1990s (FIG. 7-17 AND

Fig. 7-17. The V-22 *Osprey* in action. (Courtesy Bell-Boeing)

PLATE 5). The V-22 will be based on much of the experience gained with the Bell XV-15 which has been flying for almost a decade. All four military services are interested in the capabilities offered by the *Osprey* and it is being developed to meet the requirements of each service.

Satisfying the needs of four services results in some rather demanding design specifications (FIG. 7-18). For example, the Marine Corps' need to carry 24 troops and a couple of gunners over a range of 400 miles will determine the size of the *Osprey*. The Navy's need to stow the craft in a ship's below-deck hangar requires the rotors to be folded over the wing, the engines inclined forward, and the wings swung so that they lie in line with the fuselage—and all this has to be done in less than two minutes. Because all services must be able to deploy aircraft worldwide, the *Ospreys* will have the capability to fly unrefueled from California to Hawaii, after taking off in the STOL mode.

Advances in technology make the *Osprey* feasible now. The airframe will be made almost entirely of composites, which not only help solve the aeroelasticity problems that have plagued past V/STOL designs but also significantly reduce airframe weight. Digital fly-by-wire flight controls will replace conventional hydraulic and mechanical controls, and there will be a fully integrated cockpit.

The *Osprey* will be powered by twin gas-turbine engines connected to prop-rotors. Although it will take off like a helicopter, in horizontal flight it will fly like a turboprop, with speeds exceeding 300 MPH. The aircraft's ceiling will approach 30,000 feet, considerably higher than most helicopters, and its propulsion systems will be cross-connected to allow single-engine operation.

Delivery of operational aircraft should be in late 1991. The Marines, who plan to buy about 500 *Ospreys* for combat-assault and assault-support missions, will be the first to receive the aircraft. The Navy's order for 50 aircraft will be for search and rescue missions, though it could possibly order 300 more for antisubmarine-warfare duties. The Air Force initially plans to buy about 80 for its special-operations missions. Finally, the Army currently needs over 200 V/STOLs for missions ranging from combat assault to medical evacuation.

X-Wing. Another V/STOL with great potential, now technologically possible, is the X-wing (FIG. 7-19 AND PLATE 6). It is also referred to as the "stopped-rotor" because of the way the rotor, used for helicopter-like flight, is stopped in flight to serve as wings for fast forward flight.

Currently, the Navy is interested in the concept for its anti-submarine, airborne electronic-warfare, electronic-intelligence, and combat search-and-rescue missions. These missions are typically conducted at sea, either from aircraft carriers or other surface ships. The V/STOL capabilities permit operations to be completely done from smaller ships, which frees up the carriers to support attack and fighter aircraft and disperses the V/STOLs over a larger area of the ocean closer to their targets.

Because the Soviet submarine fleet is fast, difficult to detect, and equipped with long-range antishipping missiles, American antisubmarine-warfare aircraft must be able to travel faster and farther to negate the submarine threat. Speed and range are especially important in the search-and-rescue business. The X-wings, with forward speeds in the high-subsonic region, aircraft-like ranges, plus hover and vertical flight capabilities, could be just the ticket for future defense needs.

One major obstacle facing the designers was how to keep the aircraft from rolling over during the 30-second period when the rotor stops (or starts) during the transition between helicopter and fixed-wing modes. The answer was circulation control, often referred to as the Coanda principle, consisting of air forced through openings in the leading and trailing edges of the airfoil. The amount of air forced out determines the circulation around the wing and the lift produced. By finely controlling the circulation, stable flight can be achieved even during transition.

Circulation control also replaces much of the mechanical complexity found in helicopter rotor systems. With the X-wing as currently envisioned, it would be used for cyclic lift control, eliminating the mechanical pitching of the rotor blades during each cycle of rotation. In fixed-wing flight, it would

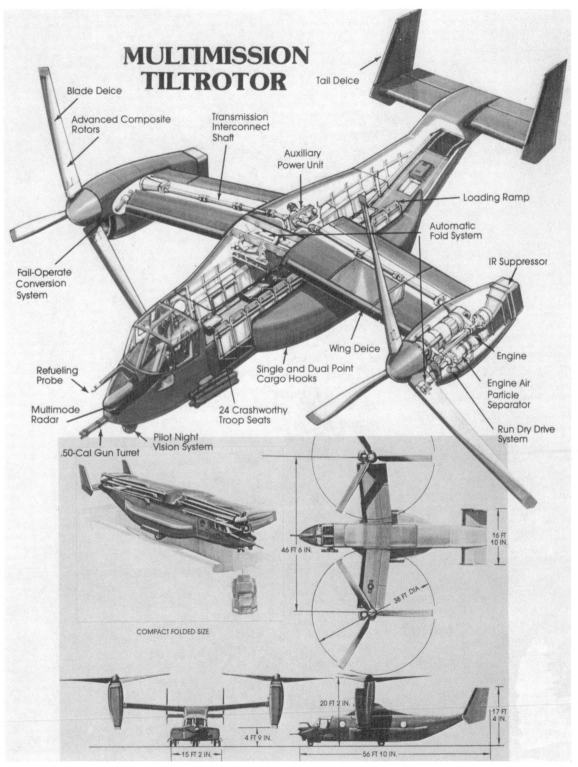

Fig. 7-18. The tilt-rotor *Osprey* would be used by all four armed services for a variety of military missions. (Courtesy Bell-Boeing)

be used for pitch control in conjunction with a horizontal stabilizer.

The entire propulsion system for the X-wing is a challenging design. Not only must it provide power to rotate the rotor, but also supply thrust for forward flight and compressed air for the circulation control.

The next step in the X-wing's development is a flight test of a circulation-control rotor including the critical transitioning sequence. To do this, Sikorsky Aircraft will be installing a stopped-rotor on its Rotor System Research Aircraft, a very sophisticated helicopter test bed used for the past decade to try out new helicopter rotor concepts. If everything goes right, an X-wing concept demonstrator could be flying by 1990 with operational X-wings in production by the year 2000.

After more than four decades of research, helicopter V/STOL will be a reality, the result of the needs being pressing and the technology being ready. You might also see previous V/STOL concepts tried again. Past failures could now be successful designs.

HELICOPTERS

The helicopter is a major part of the U.S. Army, doing everything from scouting and reconnaissance to delivering troops into battle and destroying tanks (FIG. 7-20). In the past few years the Army has purchased new helicopters such as the AH-64 *Apache* attack helicopter and the UH-60 *Blackhawk* utility helicopter. Next it plans to modernize its huge fleet of light helicopters, which currently includes the UH-1 *Huey,* AH-1 *Huey Cobra,* OH-6 *Cayuse,* and OH-58 *Kiowa.* These helicopters lack the capability to perform in the post-1990s combat environment (PLATE 8). Helicopters like the venerable *Huey* will, however, probably still be flying in the 21st century, if not with U.S. forces, at least in the multitude of foreign nations that have been supplied with the *Huey.* When it comes to helicopters, the *Huey* is as much a classic as the DC-3 "Gooney Bird" and the P-51 *Mustang.*

Fig. 7-20. This advanced helicopter would use circulation control to eliminate the need for a tail rotor. (Courtesy Hughes Helicopters)

The Army's new light helicopter now goes by the name of the Light Helicopter Family, or LHX for short. Later it will be given an official designation, and like almost every Army chopper, an Indian tribe name.

The Army is planning two versions of the LHX, a scout attack (SCAT) version and a light-utility model. The major design differences would be in the basic fuselage. The SCAT version would be for such missions as surveillance and reconnaissance, escorting troop-carrying helicopters, and attacking enemy targets. To do this, it would be equipped with "smart" missiles, rockets, and machine guns. The light-utility version would be used for transporting less than full-squad-size combat groups as well as the myriad of jobs the term "utility" implies.

The LHX must be able to survive on the "dirty" battlefield of the 1990s. This means the LHX will be designed to operate in nuclear, biological, and chemical environments. The LHX will also be designed to minimize detection, and if detected, limit destruction by enemy fire. For survivability, ballistic tolerance and protection are important. To survive ground fire, "nap-of-the-Earth" flying is a must. Then if all of this fails, the LHX must be crashworthy to limit crew and passenger casualties.

The LHX's technology is feasible today, and in many cases, has already been demonstrated and is available. One of the major changes in the LHX/SCAT from previous Army helicopters is the elimination of the co-pilot, which dramatically reduces life-cycle costs and helps overcome a predicted shortage of pilots. Sophisticated electronics will be needed for a single pilot to function adequately; these could include an integrated cockpit, automated navigation and targeting, digital maps, sensor fusion, wide field-of-view optics, and workload-reducing digital flight-control systems. To perform missions in all types of weather, even at night, the LHX will have forward-looking infrared (FLIR) capabilities, daylight TV, and a laser rangefinder/designator.

AIRLIFT TRANSPORTS

The best military strategies and tactics are of little value if the right men, weapons, and supplies cannot be in the right place at the right time. This is where strategic and tactical airlift aircraft come into play. Throughout the history of air power, airlift aircraft have not always received the attention they should have, perhaps because they are not as glamorous as fighters and bombers and do not usually push the state of aviation technology. Also, in many cases the military has simply depended on slightly modified versions of civilian commercial airliners to do the job. This has been the case from the Douglas DC-3 which became the C-47 to the

Fig. 7-21. A militarized version of a spanloader or flying wing. (Courtesy Lockheed Georgia)

Douglas DC-10 which is currently on active duty with the Air Force as the KC-10. With the scarcity of resources projected for the future, this situation will probably not change.

Aircraft like the Lockheed C-5, C-141, and the C-130 will see many more years of service. The first C-130 flew in 1954 and the 1800th aircraft rolled off the production line in 1986 (and production continues). Versions of the C-130 have ranged from gunships to stretched commercial versions. C-130s are popular aircraft with military and commercial operators around the world. Thus C-130s will be a familiar sight in the 21st century as will the giant C-5 which will still be needed to carry outsized cargo, such as Army tanks and howitzers, around the globe.

Be assured, however, that while the basic appearance of these aircraft will remain constant, the insides, especially the avionics, will be continually updated.

As in the past, there will be military versions of new commercial airliners (see Chapter 8). Items like propfans, winglets, and laminar-flow control are as beneficial to the military as to the civilian operator. If giant commercial cargo carriers are ever built, there will certainly be a market for them in the military (FIG. 7-21).

The one portion of the military airlift mission currently receiving attention is the STOL heavy-lift transport, an aircraft that can fly from small landing areas and still carry large loads, even the Army's M-1 main battle tank, over intercontinental distances. The Air Force and McDonnell Douglas are currently developing the C-17 to fill the gap between the C-5 and C-141, which carry large loads but require long improved runways, and the C-130, which can use rather primitive facilities but cannot carry huge loads (FIG. 7-22).

One of the biggest pluses for the C-17 is its ability to land fully loaded on unsurfaced airstrips as short as 3000 feet in length. The C-17 uses a feature called an engine-blown flap (EBF) to obtain the added lift required for short-field operations. With the EBF, also called "powered lift", engine exhaust pushes the air faster around large flaps located at the trailing edge of the main wings. This additional airflow makes the wing think it is flying faster than the true airspeed of the aircraft; thus, more lift is generated. The flaps, made of titanium to resist the direct impingment of the engine exhaust, permit steep approaches—as much as five degrees—even in the worst weather. The EBF will also help while air-dropping troops and equipment because airspeeds can be reduced to as low as 132 MPH.* Incidentally, the C-17 is designed to drop up to 55,000 pounds, far more than any other U.S. airlift transport. Landing approach speeds can also be as low as 132 MPH.

Another feature of the C-17 is the way the thrust reversers work on the four turbofan engines. The reversers allow the aircraft to make a steep descent in a nosedown attitude without building up excessive airspeed. Once on the ground, they rapidly slow down the airplane. The thrust reversers are designed so that the exhaust is directed upward and forward so that dust and debris are not picked up from the ground and ingested into the engines. This is a very important feature considering the type of runways the C-17 will be using. The thrust reversers will allow the C-17 to back up for ground positioning and to maneuver quite nicely on runways only 60 feet wide—pretty good for an aircraft that is roughly the size of the DC-10 and can carry some 70 tons of cargo.

The C-17 will also have supercritical wings and winglets to improve fuel economy, and its high-

---

*As a point of history, the EBF is quite different from the upper surface blowing (USB) technique used on the defunct Boeing YC-14 advanced military STOL transport (AMST) and copied by the Soviets for their An-72 transport. With USB, the exhaust is blown from a flattened nozzle across the entire upper surface of the wing behind the engine. With the flaps lowered, a sheet of air flowing at transonic speeds remains attached to the upper surface and even curves sharply downward over the lowered flaps. The exhaust gases plus entrained free-stream air point almost vertically downward giving an almost five-fold increase in lift compared to a conventional wing of the same size. The McDonnell Douglas YC-15, the competitor to the YC-14 in the AMST program, used the EBF technique. While tests have shown that the USB is a substantially more powerful powered-lift technique compared to EBF, it is probably more expensive to implement and represents a more risky technology. Perhaps someday USB will find an application on a STOL transport built in the free world.

Fig. 7-22. Opposite: The C-17 would have the capability to carry tanks and other heavy military vehicle right to the battlefield. (Courtesy McDonnell Douglas)

impact main landing gear will be able to take rough landings. In the cockpit, there will be HUDs, CRTs, and computerized controls so that the ship will need only a pilot, copilot, and loadmaster.

The first flight of the C-17 is planned for 1990. The Military Airlift Command will receive the first of some 200 C-17s in 1992. At a cost of about $90 million per copy, the Air Force will not be able to convert all of its tactical airlift to C-17s, but will still have to rely on lower-cost airlifters like the *Hercules* or a suitable replacement (currently being studied in the Future International Military Airlifter (FIMA) and Advanced Tactical Transport programs).

There is also an interest in (1) V/STOL airlifters that would require less than 300 feet for takeoffs and (2) Super Short Takeoff and Landing (SSTOL) craft that would normally require 1500 to 3000 feet, but when the situation dictated, could use 300 feet or less by activating auxiliary thrust boosters. As a point of reference, a current, fully-loaded military transport needs 5,000-6,000 feet for takeoffs.

One intriguing vertical takeoff and landing concept being considered by Lockheed-Georgia would use eight vertical-thrust turbofan engines in the wings for takeoffs and landings (FIG. 7-23). Once the aircraft is in the air, doors would be shut over and under the turbofans so that the wings would be "clean" for high-speed flight. Turbofans located in the rear of the fuselage would be used for normal flight and could provide some additional lift during takeoff. Such an aircraft would not be flying before the year 2000.

Fig. 7-23. One of many ideas for a V/STOL transport. The vertical engines in the blended wing would provide thrust for vertical landings and takeoffs. (Courtesy Lockheed-Georgia)

LIGHTER-THAN-AIR CRAFT

Lighter-than-air (LTA) craft have been proposed and flown for centuries.

The Montgolfier brothers experimented with balloons in France more than 300 years ago, and the tales of airships of the Civil War, World War I, and World War II have been told many times. Many books and movies have been written about the era of the commercial airship, which ended with the fiery crash of the *Hindenburg*. Less well-known is the fact that the U.S Navy used airships in the 1960s as part of America's early warning system for detecting a Soviet bomber attack.

Currently, the U.S. military services are showing renewed interest in airships, and Congress is even appropriating money for LTA research. Part of this interest comes from the potential of high technology in airship fabrication and propulsion, as well as advances in electronics that could make some attractive airship concepts quite feasible. Another important reason is that an airship can do some jobs better than other systems located on land or sea, in the sky, or even in space. The airship is a natural where long-duration low-altitude surveillance is needed. The U.S. Navy is most serious about advanced airships, conducting both paper studies and actual testing. The Air Force is already using airships, and the Coast Guard is maintaining a watchful eye on LTA developments.

U.S. Navy. The advent of the low-altitude cruise missile has given an impetus to a renewed Navy interest in LTA. Even the most powerful shipboard radars cannot detect low-flying missiles over the horizon. Aircraft can do the job, but are severely limited in the time they can stay on station. An airship, however, can carry the largest and most sophisticated radars with ease, and it can stay on station for weeks at a time, even in bad weather (short of a hurricane).

The long-range missile-detection radar would generally dictate the size of the airship. The radar would be carried inside the airbag just like it was in the airborne-warning airships used by the Navy from 1957 to 1961 as part of the North American Air Defense Command. The Navy's LTAs could use "conformal" radars, where the components are part of the airship. To handle the even larger radars needed for detecting supersonic and low-flying missiles with minimum radar cross-sections, the new Navy airships would be even bigger.

Additional size would also be needed to handle the added propulsion system and fuel load required for high altitudes, faster speeds and longer missions.

The largest early-warning airships built to date were the 403-foot-long ZPG-3Ws, which contained 1.5 million cubic feet of helium (FIGS. 7-24 AND 7-25). Now experts are talking about craft perhaps twice the size of the ZPG-3Ws, with bag capacities in the range of 2–3 million cubic feet.

Composites will be used extensively especially in the gondola, and hybrid propulsion systems would be used (i.e., diesel engines for low-speed, high-efficiency cruising and turboprops for higher-speed maneuvering, flight into strong headwinds, and emergency high-speed travel). Fortunately, airships are very fuel-efficient, making them feasible for lengthy missions. Regardless, the Navy would like to be able to reprovision the LTAs in flight.

For a large target like an LTA to survive in a hostile environment, stealth technology would come into play. While most of this technology is classified, suffice it to say that things like composite materials, special paints, and electronic countermeasures could make even a gigantic airship hard to detect.

U.S. Coast Guard. The Coast Guard's needs call for a smaller airship than the Navy version, perhaps in the neighborhood of 250,000 cubic feet. The Coast Guard would like a craft that could accommodate a small crew for about a two-day mission with sufficient speed to intercept a target and for getting to and from its station at sea. The Coast Guard wants to be able to use the airship for making rescues at sea as well as transporting emergency gear to ships in distress.

The Coast Guard is also interested in unmanned "aerostats" for some of its law enforcement missions. An aerostat is an airship with two

Fig. 7-24. Opposite: Lighter-than-air craft like this ZPG-3W would use power radars to detect enemy cruise missiles. (Courtesy Goodyear Aerospace)

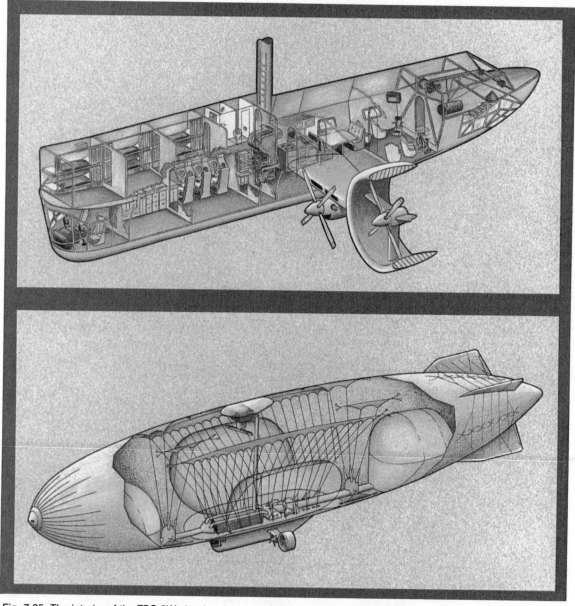

Fig. 7-25. The interior of the ZPG-3W showing the working/living compartment as well as the radar antennas inside the airbag. (Courtesy Goodyear Aerospace)

compartments separated by a bladder. The upper chamber contains helium and the lower one contains air. As the aerostat climbs, the pressure outside becomes less. Thus, the helium expands and forces air out of the lower chamber through electromechanical valves. As the aerostat descends, the helium compartment contracts and electric blowers pump air back into the lower section. This maintains both the aircraft's buoyancy and its aerodynamic shape at all altitudes.

U.S. Air Force. While the Navy and Coast Guard airships are still on the drawing board, the

Air Force has one that is operational, the tethered-aerostat radar system (TARS), deployed on the coast of southern Florida (FIG. 7-26). Because of their shape, the 250,000-cubic-foot-capacity aerostats have earned the nickname "Fat Albert."

The primary mission of TARS is detecting enemy aircraft that might attempt low-level penetration of the southern U.S. coast, but it also assists civilian drug-enforcement agencies.

The TARS craft operates at an altitude of 10,000-12,000 feet, tethered by a 25,000-foot cord. The tether is attached to a diesel-powered, locomotive-sized, launch-control vehicle that runs on a circular track. The aerostat is kept at its proper station by moving the control vehicle around the track and reeling the tether in or out. The radar housed in the TARS pod can pick up targets at up to 150 miles. Fat Albert stays aloft for up to five days, then is brought down for refueling.

REMOTELY PILOTED VEHICLES

Throughout history, warriors have wanted to know what was happening behind enemy lines before engaging the foe in battle. Scouts and spies have ventured behind enemy lines to gather intelligence, but military men have also known for centuries that you can get the maximum amount of information and a feel for the "big picture" if you do your spying from a high place, preferably the sky. Thus, balloons were used during the Civil War, and the airplane's first mission was aerial reconnaissance during World War I. Aerial reconnaissance was quite routine during World War II and reached a zenith with the U-2 and SR-71 reconnaissance aircraft.

However, manned reconnaissance aircraft are expensive, not only in terms of risking lives, but also in their design and testing (FIG. 7-27). Thus, unmanned aircraft have advantages, especially aircraft that can be controlled in flight—remotely piloted vehicles (RPVs).

For many years, the Air Force had a rather successful RPV that even saw action in Vietnam. This RPV, of which there were about two-dozen different versions, was the Teledyne Ryan AGM-34. Its missions included low-level day and night reconnaissance, high-altitude surveillance, and electronic intelligence. Interestingly, it and the SR-71 were the only air vehicles allowed to overfly North Vietnam for reconnaissance after the cessation of bombing in January 1973. The AGM-34s were either ground-launched or launched from an aircraft.

The Israelis have the most recent experience. They used RPVs in the 1973 Arab-Israeli War to "saturate" enemy air defenses, allowing Israeli fighters to go in for the kill while the Egyptians were reloading their surface-to-air missiles. More recently, RPVs, made to look "electronically" like Israeli aircraft, were used to keep Syrian gunners busy while Israeli reconnaissance airplanes flying at higher altitudes collected intelligence data on Syrian missile sites. On other occasions, while Syrian radars were tracking the RPVs, the Israelis fired anti-radiation missiles at ground missile sites by homing in on the radar signature. They also used RPVs for near-real-time reconnaissance of vital ground targets destined for air attacks. The Israelis found RPVs to be essentially immune to enemy action because of their small size and minimum radar signature.

With today's high technology in computers, sensors, and communications equipment, RPVs can be even more effectively used for reconnaissance and surveillance, communications relay, mine detection, and weather data collection. They can be used to detect targets and then, with laser beams, designate the targets for destruction by laser-guided missiles and bombs. Key intelligence can be obtained on enemy communication and radar systems to determine the enemy's order of battle. With jammers installed, they can be used in an electronic warfare role. By installing ordnance they can even be used for direct attacks on the enemy.

Today, the U.S. Army's *Aquila*, built by Lockheed, is probably the world's most sophisticated

Fig. 7-26. (Page 138) "Fat Albert" helps detect drug smugglers as well as enemy aircraft. (Courtesy U.S. Air Force)

Fig. 7-27. (Page 139) This manned reconnaissance aircraft could reach Mach 5 at a maximum altitude of 100,000 feet. (Courtesy Lockheed-California)

RPV (FIG. 7-28). The *Aquila* is a 260-pound machine, made mostly of preimpregnated Kevlar-epoxy, so that the enemy will have a hard time detecting it by radar. The flying-wing shape also helps.

The *Aquila* can fly at speeds of up to 114 MPH at altitudes of up to 12,000 feet. Its two-bladed, pusher propeller is powered by a 26-horsepower, two-cylinder engine. Currently, the *Aquila's* payload includes a daylight, black-and-white TV camera and laser rangefinders/target designators for target location, acquisition, and designation, as well as reconnaissance.

The *Aquila* is launched using a hydraulically operated catapult mounted on a five-ton truck. After a mission is completed, the RPV is recovered by flying it into a vertical net that is mounted on another truck. *Aquila's* pusher propeller is encased in a shroud so that it does not get entangled in the net. The nerve center for the *Aquila* system is the ground control station which controls the RPV and processes its data. The entire *Aquila* system is mobile so that it can be moved relatively easily as the battlefield location changes.

The disadvantage of fixed-wing RPVs like the *Aquila* is their need for a complex launcher and a runway, net, or parachute for recovery if they are to be used again. One way to get around this problem is to use an RPV that operates like a helicopter, the remotely piloted helicopter (RPH). Today, there are many RPH projects under development like Canadair's CL-227, which can take off and land vertically, as well as fly at horizontal speeds of up to 80 MPH at altitudes of up to 10,000 feet (FIGS. 7-29 AND 7-30). It can even hover over a target while performing its mission. This Canadian-developed RPH uses two contrarotating rotors, eliminating the need for a tail rotor. The CL-227 is powered by a small gas turbine engine that burns diesel fuel. Its hour-glass shape keeps its radar detectability to a minimum, as do its radar-absorbing body materials and Kevlar rotors. The CL-227 can be launched and recovered from a truck or even the deck of a small ship.

Modern, miniaturized, electronic technology and advanced materials are making practical and potent RPV systems possible. State-of-the-art devices like very small day-and-night TV cameras, laser designators, and navigation and communication systems are being used in RPVs. Electronics also make RPVs easier to control from the ground. Autopilots and radio or inertial navigation systems keep the RPV at the right altitude and attitude, and on the right track to and from the target. The RPV "pilot" only has to command the RPV when unprogrammed changes are required.

RPVs can sneak up on the enemy because of their small size and essentially noiseless operation. Low radar and infrared signatures make them hard to detect even by sophisticated sensors. Remotely piloted vehicles are just another example where advanced technology can be used to counter a numerically superior enemy. RPVs allow the ground commander to look deep into enemy territory, and in some cases the RPV lets him do something about it.

High costs have been one of the biggest impediments to RPVs being used to their full potential. Advocates often tout the RPV as a "low-cost" solution to military problems. But experience has shown otherwise. When designs of RPVs begin they usually have low acquisition and operational costs as goals. However, along the way to development things happen to drive up costs.

First of all, the military services want the RPVs to do a multitude of jobs. Then they demand super reliability and want to use people with a minimum of experience and training to operate them. All this adds up to complex, heavy, sophisticated, and expensive RPVs. As they become very valuable, they must be made reusable, and this increases the complexity and cost of the ground equipment. Before you know it, system costs of the RPV approach those of the manned system it was designed to replace. At that point the military would much rather have a manned system with all its inherent advantages.

Now, with low-cost miniaturized electronics, low-cost RPVs can be designed and built. But the military manager must make sure that the project

Fig. 7-28. Opposite: The *Aquila* remotely piloted vehicle has a flying-wing configuration to help reduce observables. (Courtesy Lockheed Missile and Space Company)

is kept on course and not add "nice but not necessary" capabilities or to try to accomplish a multitude of different missions. Perhaps an RPV could be designed for only a few uses or could even be expendable. In the heat of battle, a commander would probably rather have many simple RPVs at his disposal versus a few expensive ones. The loss of one or two of the latter would represent a significant portion of his assets. Also because RPVs are unmanned, less stringent requirements should be placed on componentry. Simplicity reduces electrical power requirements which have a direct bearing on system weight.

The cost of the air vehicle and ground equipment could, however, be better amortized over a large number of multipurpose units. Different black boxes or cassettes could be inserted into the same air vehicle depending on the mission. (Note that this is different from a single, complex RPV that could do many things.) There would be different payloads for day and night reconnaissance, as well as a different module for laser target designation. Payload module changes would be simple enough that they could be done right in the field.

Fig. 7-29. You can see why the CL-227 remotely piloted helicopter has earned the nickname "Peanut". (Courtesy Canadair)

Finally, there are other reasons to justify RPVs,

Fig. 7-30. Another RPH that could be used for surveillance and reconnaissance behind enemy lines. (Courtesy Westland Helicopters)

for example, not having men overfly high-threat environments or incurring the political implications of having a manned craft shot down over a hostile or neutral nation. However, if these are the reasons for RPV development they should be clearly stated, and the program should not be sold on the economy argument.

SOLAR-POWERED AIRCRAFT

The military has become highly dependent on space satellites to supply vital data, from intelligence to weather forecasts. But there is a limit to what satellites can do, especially if you want continuous coverage of a particular area on the Earth's surface. The only way you can do this from space without using a multitude of satellites in different orbits is to place the satellite in geosynchronous orbit some 22,000 miles above the Earth's surface. Not only is it very expensive to launch satellites into this high orbit, but pictures taken at this height often lack enough detail. The answer is an aircraft that can loiter on the fringe's of the Earth's atmosphere for long periods of time.

Solar-powered aircraft show strong potential for long-duration, continuous coverage at relatively low cost. Thus, NASA and Lockheed have been investigating the potential of the Solar High-Altitude Powered Platform (Solar HAPP) (FIG. 7-31).

The Solar HAPP would be a very large, but light, unmanned aircraft that could stay aloft for up to a year. It would loiter at an altitude of about 65,000 feet where scientists have determined the winds are calmest. While less power would be needed to overcome winds, the aircraft would need extremely large wing surfaces to provide enough lift in the rarified atmosphere.

To keep weight down to two tons for an aircraft with a wingspan of over 300 feet, it must be made of very lightweight materials, such as graphite epoxy for the structure, and Mylar and Teflon for the wing covering. The craft must also be strong; at an altitude of twelve miles, there are still air turbulence and wind gusts to contend with.

The HAPP has to take off and land on the ground. The plan is to launch it on a very calm day, taking up to four hours to spiral up to the desired operating altitude. During daylight, solar cells on the HAPP would capture sunlight and convert it to electrical power. This power would be used directly during the day and also charge fuel cells needed for nighttime operation. The wingtips would be folded down at night to provide better aerodynamics and reduce power requirements. The slow-turning pusher propeller would be powered by an electric motor, and the craft would have a maximum speed of just over 90 MPH.

While the original Lockheed studies concentrated on a Solar HAPP vehicle for monitoring agriculture over the southwestern U.S., the military applications for surveillance and communications relay are quite obvious.

Throughout military history, there has been a clear understanding of the need to take the high ground and hold it. Since World War I, this has included controlling the air over the battlefield. The potency of air superiority was proven when the Royal Air Force, by controlling the sky over England, prevented Germany from invading England in World War II. It was reported that Hermann Goring, the head of the Luftwaffe, realized that Germany had lost the war when he saw allied fighters over Berlin. The wings of the future in all their various forms mean military superiority in the 21st century. Hopefully, their existence alone will deter any aggressor from ever putting them to the test.

Fig. 7-31. (Page 144) A solar-powered RPV could be flown at extremely high altitudes for up to a year at a time. (Courtesy Lockheed Missile and Space Company)

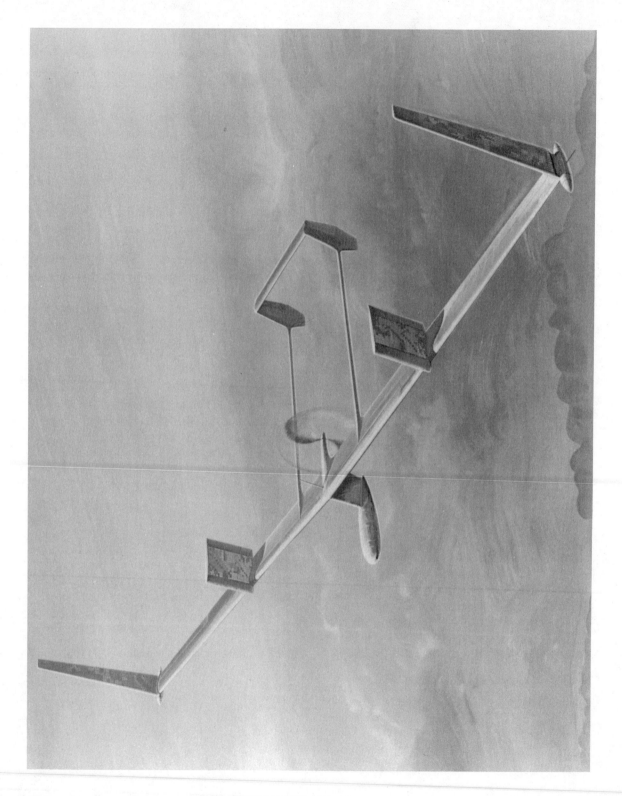

8

Commercial Aircraft

THE AIRLINE INDUSTRY'S ACCEPTANCE of new aircraft and new technology is keyed to profitability and safety. Profitability can come from both reduced operating costs and extra services for which a substantial number of people are willing to pay a surcharge. Safety can be actual or perceived. Airline travelers may not want to fly in airliners that, despite their safety, look too unusual (FIGS. 8-1 AND 8-2).

Air cargo, on the other hand, is not choosy. So air-freight and air-express carriers might be the most influential force in commercial aircraft design of the 21st century. Air cargo could well be the reason for building giant supersonic and hypersonic aircraft.

SUPERSONIC TRANSPORTS

Except for the *Concorde*, previous SSTs were thwarted by economics and the environmental concerns of noise pollution and sonic boom problems. Even the *Concorde* is limited in the routes it can economically fly, the airports at which it is allowed

to land, and the speeds at which it can fly over land (FIG. 8-3). Advances in technology could overcome these problems.

A future supersonic transport could travel at speeds of Mach 2.7, making a trip from Los Angeles to Tokyo in a little over three hours (FIG. 8-4). To reduce fuel consumption, the factor that plagues the *Concorde*'s economy, a very slender body design could be coupled with a low-aspect-ratio wing to greatly reduce wave drag. For further drag reduction, active laminar-control techniques, such as those that suck off the boundary layer, could be used. Wing-body blending, as found on military aircraft, would also improve aerodynamics.

Advanced materials and structural design would be used to reduce aircraft weight, another major ingredient in the profitability equation. For example, by replacing traditional skin-stringer titanium structures with superplastic-formed, diffusion-bonded sandwich construction (that eliminates separate stringers and ribs), structural weights could be halved. In this technique, flat

Fig. 8-1. The Boeing 7J7 represents the conventional subsonic airliners that will be flying in the 21st century. While rather traditional in design, it will have much new technology in propulsion, materials, and avionics. (Courtesy Boeing)

sheets of titanium are heated in a mold until they become plasticized. Then they are blown into corrugated sandwich-like structures that are diffusion-bonded into the final shape. An added benefit of this process is improved resistance to fatigue, leading to much longer airframe life.

Propulsion systems for an SST are quite different from the typical high-bypass-ratio engines used in subsonic airliners to get good fuel economy. For sustained supersonic operation, low-bypass-ratio, high-thrust-to-weight-ratio engines are needed. Fortunately, such engines are being developed for military aircraft. Because of the wide speed range of an SST, combined cycle engines could be a very logical candidate.

France is reportedly working on a second-generation *Concorde*. This 200-passenger airplane, planned for the year 2000, would be faster and twice as efficient as the current fuel-guzzling model. High-technology variable-cycle engines, with a bypass mode, provide the better economy at subsonic speeds.

Because of the low bypass ratios needed for supersonic operation, air travels much faster through an SST's engine than a high-bypass subsonic engine. This higher velocity results in substantially

Fig. 8-2. Opposite: Subsonic transports of the 21st century might resemble this fuel-efficient turboprop concept, complete with canards and aft-located main wings. (Courtesy NASA)

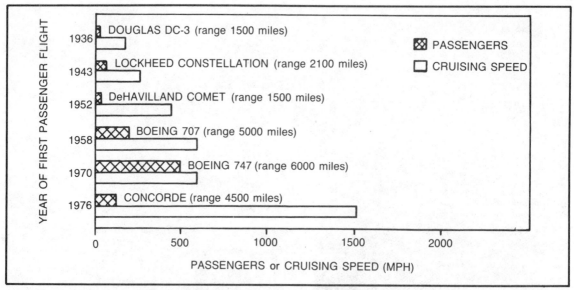

Fig. 8-3. Though faster, the *Concorde* carries fewer passengers than many other transports.

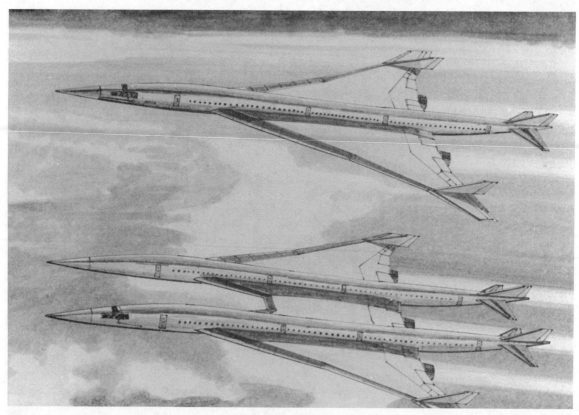

Fig. 8-4. A new supersonic transport could carry 250 passengers across the Pacific in just over three hours. Both single- and dual-fuselage designs have been considered. (Courtesy NASA)

higher noise levels. Some of this noise can be reduced by careful design of the engine inlets and nozzles. Also, by using high-thrust-to-weight characteristics in conjunction with automatic throttle controls, the SST could accelerate faster to its best climb speed and thus exit the airport area sooner. For example, takeoff speed for an SST could be 250 MPH or higher compared to about 200 MPH for a subsonic airliner. Likewise, descents during landing approaches could be steeper. While noise on the runway would still be higher, noise offensive to the airport's neighbors might be less than today's airliners. Engineers are investigating more sophisticated flight techniques that could result in substantial noise reduction.

As for the sonic boom problem, studies have shown that the overpressure caused by supersonic speeds can be reduced to half of that of previous U.S. designs by choosing an optimum shape for the SST. It still remains to be seen if this would be low enough to satisfy the general public.

One idea for an SST that has been bandied about for several years is the scissor- or oblique-wing concept explained in Chapter 3. The scissor wing could provide optimum performance under all SST flight conditions (PLATE 14).

A slender scissor wing would require much less power at low speeds than a delta-wing SST which compensates for its high drag and lack of lift by much greater thrust, with its attendant high fuel consumption and noise levels. The scissor wing would be especially attractive if the SST must overfly continents subsonically; its fuel efficiency at high subsonic speeds would be much improved over the delta wing. The scissor-wing concept has been successfully tested subsonically in prototype form with the manned AD-1, which has flown with its wing yawed as much as 60 degrees.

The "oblique flying wing" takes the scissor-wing idea one step further by eliminating the fuselage. Passengers would ride within the wing itself. To accommodate 250 passengers on eight rows of seats facing the leading edge of the wing, the wing must have a chord of 50 to 60 feet and a maximum thickness of 7 feet. The angle of wing sweep would be maintained by rudders that would steer the wing;

the engines would also possibly have to be pivoted. However, successful landings of the AD-1 with its wings yawed at 45 degrees indicate that yaw, and thus thrust direction changes, might be small enough that they could be accomplished simply by thrust vectoring.

The advantages of the oblique flying wing are its very high lift-to-drag ratios compared to conventional SSTs such as the *Concorde*. High lift-to-drag at both subsonic and supersonic speeds means less power is needed. Computations show that this flying wing could be as fuel efficient as the Boeing 747 and have a greater range than the *Concorde*.

HYPERSONIC TRANSPORTS

Some experts believe that the supersonic transport should be leap frogged directly to a hypersonic transport which would travel at Mach 5-10 (FIG. 8-5). This is about 4000-8000 MPH at a cruising altitude of 150,000 feet. Here the supersonic boom would cease to cause problems to the people on the ground below.

Although the U.S. is developing the technology for a hypersonic aircraft, or what President Reagan referred to as the "Orient Express," Americans are not the only ones interested in ultra-high-speed transports—so are the Europeans, Russians, and Japanese. France is pursuing the *Hermes*, a vertically-launched design that looks somewhat like the U.S. Space Shuttle. The French hope to have the *Hermes* in operation by 1995.

The British are working on the HOTOL (Horizontal Takeoff and Landing) aerospace vehicle, which could serve both as a space launcher and as a 60-passenger airliner that could travel from London to Sydney in under 70 minutes (FIG. 8-6 AND PLATE 11). The key part of the HOTOL is a new powerplant from Rolls-Royce that, in space, would operate on liquid hydrogen and oxygen, like a rocket. In the atmosphere, it would work like a ramjet on liquid hydrogen and get its oxygen by "scooping" it up through a variable-geometry inlet. The British are planning a two-thirds-scale test prototype for the mid-1990s. The full-scale HOTOL probably could not be in operation until the year 2005.

The Germans recently announced that they were working on a combination space shuttle and hypersonic airliner. The German design would operate from conventional runways, have turna-round times of days instead of weeks or months, and be able to deliver payloads to low earth orbit for less cost than the Space Shuttle or even *Hermes*.

The Japanese are getting into the space busi-ness in a big way and are even in the initial phases of a space transportation system resembling the Space Shuttle, but smaller. Naturally, the Japanese could use this technology to develop a high-speed airliner.

And, even though they do not talk much about it; the Soviets most likely are working on versions of space shuttles and hypersonic aircraft. We know that the Soviets have flight tested a sub-scale model of what might be their space shuttle.

LARGE COMMERCIAL TRANSPORTS

While very large passenger airliners capable of carrying many hundreds or even thousands of pas-sengers will probably never be built, there is definitely a market for very large cargo aircraft. These air freighters would fill the gap between to-day's cargo aircraft and surface ships.

While aircraft will never be able to replace or even economically compete with huge-capacity sur-face ships, they do offer the advantage of speed.

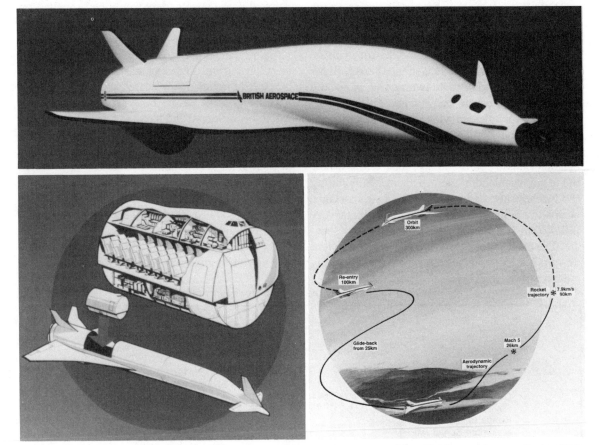

Fig. 8-6. The HOTOL, a British hypersonic transport, would use a passenger module, allowing rapid conversion to satisfy a variety of missions. The aircraft would be launched horizontally into orbit, then glide back to Earth.

Even the slowest of the proposed huge aircraft provides a tenfold increase in speed over surface craft, an important consideration where cargo is perishable, of high value, or must be delivered to market rapidly. Most large-aircraft concepts are being proposed for international and transoceanic transportation.

As a yardstick for comparing these huge aircraft, Table 8-1 lists the characteristics of three of the largest air transports in service today, the Lockheed C-5 military airlifter, the cargo version of the Boeing 747, and the Soviet Antonov An-124. The last is markedly similar to the C-5, but not surprisingly so, because it has the same mission, strategic airlift of large and outsized loads.

Spanloaders

Spanloaders use the same basic design as the flying-wing bombers of the 1940s and 1950s, and for essentially the same reason (FIG. 8-7). As the weight of an aircraft fuselage and the cargo inside grows, the wings must be longer and thicker. Bending loads at the wing roots (where the wings and fuselage meet) become tremendous. The wings become thick enough to provide cavernous cargo compartments and eliminate the need for a fuselage. By distributing the load over the entire wingspan, bending loads are substantially reduced (this is how the term "spanloader" comes about). Eliminating the fuselage also reduces drag because fuselages normally are drag producers and contribute very little to the overall lift of an aircraft.

The spanloader turns out to be a very efficient design. For example, in today's air freighter only about 10 to 25 percent of the total gross weight is revenue-producing cargo. The rest is structure, engines, fuel, etc. One spanloader design from Boeing would weigh on the order of three million pounds, of which one million pounds could be cargo. For very large spanloaders, studies have shown that the payload can be as much as 50 percent of the total takeoff weight.

The greatly improved structural efficiency would come not only from the distributed wing loading, but also from the extensive use of composite materials. Active control systems would be used to reduce stresses during turbulence and maneuvering. And because high speeds are not planned, the wings could be straight versus swept. Supercritical wings would also probably be used, their thick characteristics adding to the payload capacity. Typically, the spanloaders would be propelled by six, eight, or even more engines, probably fueled with hydrogen.

The spanloaders lend themselves to very efficient loading and unloading techniques. They would be loaded through doors located in the wingtips. As with many large cargo-transport concepts, cargo would be packaged and handled most efficiently in containers. These containers would be standardized and could be carried by trucks, trains, or even ships to their final destinations.

The huge spanloaders are not without their problems, the most significant one being the huge wingspan—350 to 500 feet. This means the spanloaders could not operate from conventional runways, which are neither wide enough nor sufficiently strong to bear the huge load.

Table 8-1. Today's Three Largest Transport Aircraft.

	Lockheed C-5B	Boeing 747F	Antonov An-124
Wingspan (ft)	223	196	240
Length (ft)	247	232	228
Gross Weight (lb)	800,000	820,000	893,000
Payload (lb)	264,700	269,600	331,000
Range (miles)	2729	6000	3100
Maximum Speed (MPH)	571	600	537

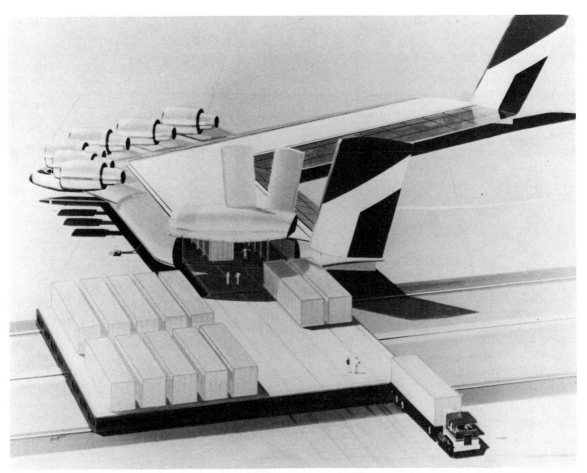

Fig. 8-7. A spanloader air freighter would allow rapid loading and unloading. (Courtesy Lockheed Georgia)

Several solutions have been proposed to get around this problem. Special hub airports could be built in a few locations to handle the spanloaders, and smaller feeder aircraft would deliver the cargo to and from the hub. However, this would add to the transit time.

Another idea is to use air-cushion landing gear in place of wheels. Riding on a cushion of air, the spanloader's weight could be distributed over a large area so that it could land and taxi on soft ground, ice, or snow. Or, the craft could land and take off from the water, and use the air-cushion equipment for taxiing on land to and from the terminal. When not needed, the air-cushion gear could be retracted into the wing to reduce drag.

Multibody Aircraft

One way of getting around the runway problems of a large aircraft is to use two or three fuselages joined by main and tail wings (FIGS. 8-8 AND 8-9 AND PLATE 15). The multiple-fuselage aircraft could increase the structural efficiency of spanloaders by distributing weight better than a conventional single-fuselage aircraft. Only the outer wings are cantilevered while the wing sections between the fuselages are simply supported. The cargo would be carried in the fuselages rather than the wings, which would be reserved mainly for fuel.

The multibody air freighters would not be as aerodynamically efficient as the spanloaders because they would still have drag-producing

153

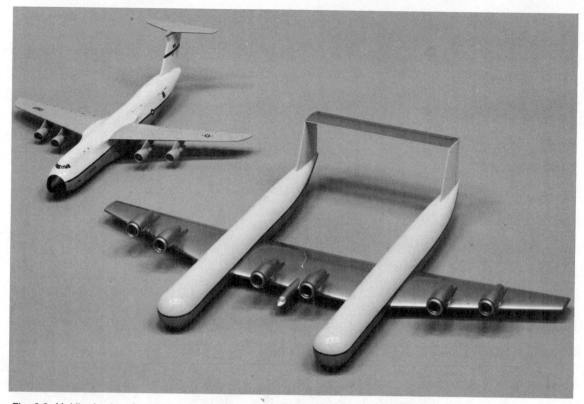

Fig. 8-8. Multibody aircraft could have lighter wing structure than a single-fuselage aircraft with the same capacity. A giant by today's standards, the C-5 is shown for comparison. (Courtesy Lockheed-Georgia)

fuselages, but they would be less expensive to develop and build. Some of the concepts proposed by airframe manufacturers consist of fuselages from currently produced airliners joined together in catamaran fashion. The development of new fuselage designs would be largely alleviated. Also, because production costs per unit go down as production rates go up, the production of two or three of essentially the same fuselage for a single aircraft would take advantage of this fact. Loading of two or three fuselages might be accomplished in a shorter time than just one fuselage holding the same cargo volume.

The catamaran-type aircraft is not a new idea. The twin-hulled Savoia-Marchetti SM-55 and SM-66 were built in Italy in the 1930s, and after World War II, two P-51 fuselages were joined together to make the very-long-range F-82 fighter.

Flatbed

The flatbed transport concept is borrowed from the tractor-trailer that revolutionized motor trucking many decades ago. The flatbed consists of an abbreviated fuselage that essentially contains only the crew compartment. Behind this is the cargo area that, in its basic form, consists of a completely flat area.

If outsized cargo such as heavy machinery or construction equipment were to be carried, it would simply be loaded on the flatbed, lashed down, and flown exposed. Naturally, the drag would be higher than with a streamlined fuselage, but that is the penalty to be paid for carrying cargo that cannot be loaded within a conventional aircraft fuselage (FIG. 8-10).

Containerized cargo would be loaded directly on the flatbed without any outer covering. To re-

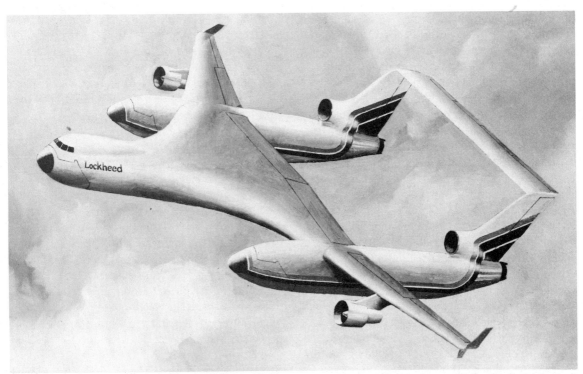

Fig. 8-9. In this multibody cargo carrier, 50 percent of the cargo would be carried in the center fuselage, and the rest would be split between the two outboard sections. (Courtesy Lockheed-Georgia)

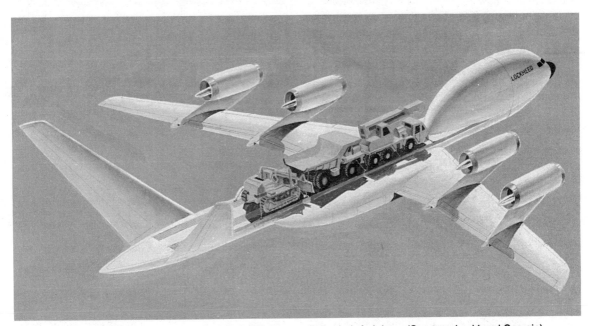

Fig. 8-10. Outsized cargo could be carried in the open on a flatbed air freighter. (Courtesy Lockheed-Georgia)

duce drag, the containers themselves could be designed so that, when fitted together, they would function as a streamlined fuselage (FIG. 8-11). This would eliminate the need for a conventional fuselage and the resultant weight penalty. For cargo requiring a pressurized or temperature-controlled environment, a removable "cocoon" could be fit over the containers, or the containers themselves could be insulated and pressurized.

Finally, the flatbed transport could be easily converted to a passenger-carrying airliner by loading a passenger module on top of the flatbed. Furthermore, this module could be loaded and unloaded at the passenger terminal and wheeled out to the flatbed, like an advanced version of the mobile-lounge concept used at Dulles International Airport near Washington, D.C. Such an idea would reduce terminal congestion and mean smaller airport terminals because the aircraft could stay out on the flight line. The passenger module could even be loaded on wheels and driven on the road or over a track to provide transportation between the airport and the inner city.

The flatbed would be a truly efficient convertible airliner, something that airline operators have sought for years. It could haul passengers during the peak daytime hours and freight at night. And the conversion could take place very rapidly.

Wing-in-Ground-Effect

An aircraft flying very close to the surface of the Earth gets a sizable boost in lift from the cushion of air compressed between the wings and surface. However, because this surface effect extends only to an altitude of about one-half the wingspan, the wingspan would have to be large enough to permit the aircraft to fly at a safe distance above the surface. Thus, the wing-in-ground-effect (WIG) idea is best suited to very large aircraft. And because the only locations where long-range travel can be made over smooth surfaces is over oceans, a WIG aircraft would also have to be a seaplane (FIGS. 8-12 AND 8-13).

While the ground effect of a large WIG aircraft would be felt a hundred feet or so "off the deck," the most dramatic increase in lift occurs if the aircraft flies at an altitude of 10 to 20 feet. This might seem a bit dangerous, but the surface effect has a stabilizing effect. If the aircraft flies too low, the lift increases, causing the aircraft to climb a bit. If the altitude becomes too great, lift decreases and the aircraft settles down. Likewise, in a roll the low wing has increased lift and the high wing has less lift, so the aircraft automatically returns to a level position. To reduce the loss of lift due to tip vortices, end plates, which operate like winglets, would be used. These end plates would literally skim over the tops of the waves.

One recent wrinkle to the WIG idea is the addition of a power-augmented-ram (PAR) propulsion system. This consists of several large turbofan engines mounted on the forward part of the fuselage.

Fig. 8-11. Alternatively, a flatbed air freighter could carry containerized cargo. (Courtesy Lockheed-Georgia)

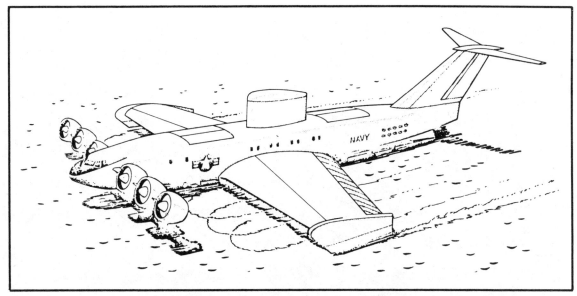

Fig. 8-12. The wing-in-ground-effect (WIG) transport would normally operate at an altitude of less than 100 feet. (Courtesy NASA)

During takeoff, these engines would be tilted so that the exhaust would raise the pressure under the wings, increasing lift and decreasing takeoff distance. While the PAR-WIG aircraft would operate most efficiently at extremely low altitudes, the aircraft could even fly over land at normal altitudes. For flight at low altitudes, speeds would be kept relatively low, for example, less than 400 MPH.

PAR-WIG aircraft with gross weights of over two million pounds and payload capacities approaching one million pounds have been considered in preliminary design studies.

Nuclear-Powered Aircraft

Every few years the idea of a very large nuclear-powered aircraft surfaces. While a nuclear-powered aircraft would have almost unlimited range and endurance, the nuclear engine could not

Fig. 8-13. Another WIG transport equally appropriate for military and commercial cargo.

Fig. 8-14. The Lockheed Omega concept would use a transverse fan propulsion system with engine inlets in the tail surfaces and fuselage. The exhaust near the trailing edge would provide STOL capability. (Lockheed-Georgia)

Fig. 8-15. The Sea Sitter with its catamaran-type fuselage. (Courtesy Lockheed-Georgia)

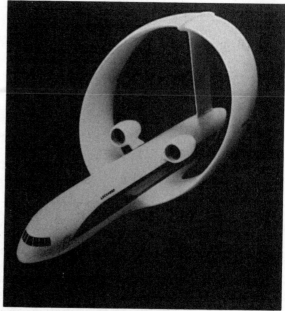

Fig. 8-16. The Ring Wing results in very high structural efficiency. (Courtesy Lockheed-Georgia)

provide enough power for takeoffs with large payloads. Because of these characteristics some interesting operational schemes have been proposed.

For takeoff, normal jet engines could be used to augment the nuclear powerplant. Aircraft with as many as 54 jet engines have been proposed to give STOL capability to a 12-million-pound aircraft.

Another idea is to use the nuclear aircraft as a tug. The nuclear aircraft would be launched without a payload and stay aloft for up to months at a time. Periodically, smaller airliners would take off fully loaded with cargo, but with a light fuel load.

Fig. 8-17. Opposite: A glimpse of an airport of the 21st century showing a variety of airliner concepts. (Courtesy Lockheed-Georgia)

158

Two or more of these conventionally powered aircraft would climb to the altitude of the nuclear-powered tug where they would hook up for a tow. Upon reaching a point near their destination they would be released to land.

Similarly, nuclear aircraft could be used as aircraft carriers. Again smaller aircraft would provide transport to and from the nuclear aircraft, but they would actually dock with the large mothership.

Because of safety considerations, flights of nuclear-powered aircraft might be restricted to over the water or an altitude high enough that the reactor could be shut down before a crash.

Whether a nuclear-powered aircraft is ever built is a matter of conjecture. Not only are there serious safety concerns, but development and fabrication costs might be prohibitively expensive. Regardless, the airports and seaplane bases of the 21st century will eventually service aircraft that today are considered rather "far out" (FIGS. 8-14 THROUGH 8-17).

9

General-Aviation Aircraft

IT IS EASIER to say what general aviation is not, than to define what it is. General aviation covers every type of piloted airborne craft that is not in service with either the military or the major commercial airlines. Even commuter, air-taxi, and private business aircraft are included. Not only does general aviation represent the largest number of aircraft, over 220,000 in the U.S. at last count, it represents the greatest diversity in technology. General-aviation aircraft range all the way from light aircraft that were built with pre-World War II technology to future supersonic business jets that currently are on the drawing boards.

Staggering lawsuit settlements and liability insurance premiums have probably hit the general-aviation market harder than any other segment of society, except for the medical profession. By 1986, the manufacturer's product-liability insurance cost per new aircraft was averaging a whopping $70,000, up from a mere $2000 in the early 1970s. Things were so bad that, by 1987, the big three general-aviation manufacturers, Cessna, Beech, and Piper, had stopped producing most lightplanes.

Legislative action, not technology, will be the solution to this problem.

As you will see, general-aviation enthusiasts and manufacturers have found ways to get around these problems, and these solutions will set the tone for general aviation well into the 21st century.

BUSINESS AIRCRAFT

High-rolling executives and celebrities demand air transportation that meets their personal needs; they do not want to tailor their schedules around the timetables of the commercial airlines. This has created a flourishing demand for executive transports (FIGS. 9-1 THROUGH 9-3). And if hijackings and terrorism continue, important people will find that only private air transportation can provide the security they desire.

Because of this expanding market, new business aircraft are starting to roll off the production lines, with many more on the drawing board and in various stages of development. Many will also serve in the commuter-airline and air-taxi markets, albeit with more spartan interiors than the plush

Fig. 9-1. The Gates *Learjet,* a rather advanced business jet, is already flying. (Courtesy Gates Learjet)

executive transports. These new aircraft include the Beech *Starship I,* the Piaggio *Avanti,* the *Omac I,* and the *Avtek 400,* being developed for today's market with today's state-of-the-art technology.

Each of these aircraft has a rather revolutionary design, reflecting the individual manufacturer's

approach to achieving a more efficient aircraft. All four have canards that reduce the lift required of the main wing. On the *Starship I,* the canard, which is computer-controlled, even has variable geometry so that it can sweep farther aft for less drag at high-speed cruise or sweep forward to provide bet-

Fig. 9-2. Another advanced business jet is the Gulfstream IV. (Courtesy Gulfstream Aerospace)

162

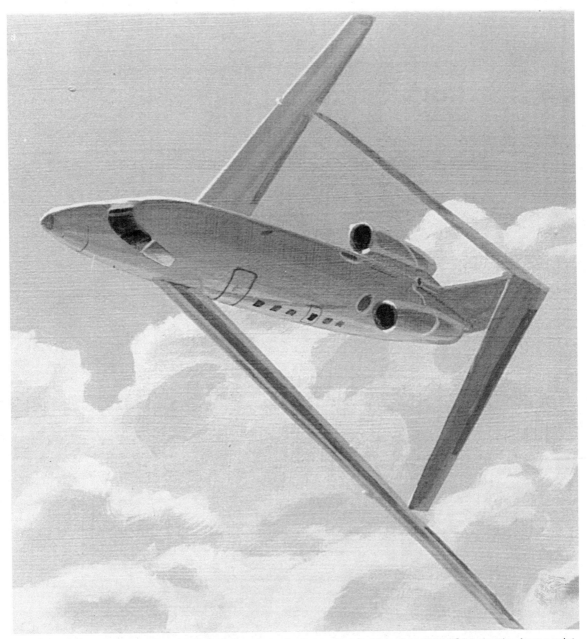

Fig. 9-3. An artist's concept of a joined-wing commuter or business aircraft. (Copyright 1984 ACA Industries from a painting by Paul Fjeld)

ter stability at low speeds (FIG. 9-4). On both the *Starship* and *Omac*, conventional tails have been replaced by large tipsails that not only provide directional stability, but also gain important drag benefits by reducing the wingtip vortices. All have

pusher propellers for better fuel economy, quieter cabins, and better control during single-engine operation (the *Omac I* is a single-engine aircraft).

Advanced materials abound in all of these futuristic aircraft. The structure of the *Starship I*

is almost completely graphite epoxy, with only a minimum of titanium in areas of high stress. To handle lightning strikes, a problem with all-composite aircraft, there is an impregnated aluminum mesh to protect the exterior. Because of the composite's high strength-to-weight ratio, not only is the aircraft lighter, but the cabin walls are only 2.5 inches thick, about half the thickness of an aluminum aircraft. This permits a more slender fuselage with less drag and without sacrificing interior room. While using composites for empennages, engine nacelles, tail cones, and canards, Piaggio still uses aluminum for the fuselage and wings. The structures of the *Avtek 400* and *Omac I* are essentially all-composite.

The cockpits of these aircraft are as modern as their external designs. In the *Starship I*, for example, great care has gone into the ergonomics of the cockpit design. Gone is the clutter found in earlier-generation business aircraft. In its place is an efficient, workload-reducing presentation of information that allows the crew to make rapid decisions and keep a clear view of the outside world.

Stepping into the pilot's "office," you immediately notice the 14 CRTs. There are only a few "old-fashioned" instruments like a gyro horizon, airspeed indicator, and altimeter, which are included as backup to the CRT displays. Twelve of the CRTs are full color with superb computer-generated graphics.

If you think the crew is treated handsomely, you should see the accommodations for the VIP riding in the rear. Hand-looped carpeting, glove-like leather, and real wood trim are the standard fare. It is not unusual to find well-equipped bars, full galleys, plush lavatories/dressing rooms, and complete video/stereo entertainment centers. These passengers travel first-class-plus.

Overall, you might say when it comes to business aircraft, the 21st century has already arrived. However, with businesses taking on global dimensions, subsonic private "airliners" may not be fast enough for high-level executives who want to hold meetings halfway around the world and return home the same day.

To meet their needs, British Aerospace, one of the builders of the *Concorde*, is exploring the possibilities of a 12-passenger business jet that could cruise at around Mach 1.8 and have a range of 3800

Fig. 9-5. A business or commuter aircraft with a propfan engine installed. (Courtesy NASA)

miles (PLATE 18). British Aerospace calls the aircraft "Concordette" because it looks somewhat like its older, big brother. Unlike *Concorde*, however, this business jet would be somewhat simpler with overwing-mounted engines and would probably not have a movable heat shield over the cockpit. British Aerospace firmly believes there will be a substantial market for supersonic executive transports in the 21st century.

LIGHTPLANES

Of all aviation, the area that might be least affected by advances in aerodynamics, materials, and propulsion technology could be single-engine light aircraft. Because of liability problems, sales of new lightplanes will probably remain in their current doldrums unless changes in laws are made. In the meantime, the lightplane builders will stick to proven designs and technology to minimize the legal problems that might come with less-established concepts and technology. Companies like Piper, Cessna, and Beech have always been pretty conservative when it comes to their lightplanes. Except perhaps for fancier paint jobs, the lightplanes commonly seen around airfields today are pretty much the same designs seen in the 1950s.

While designs, engines, and construction practices will not change drastically in the future, this will not be the case for avionics. Advances in electronics plus demands for greater safety will mean that, while lightplanes might represent 1950s' concepts, the instrument panel will keep pace with the progress of other aviation sectors.

Fortunately, innovations in the lightplane industry are not completely dead. In recent years, many smaller builders have developed some pretty radical lightplanes, often incorporating concepts pioneered by "homebuilders" (FIGS. 9-6 THROUGH 9-11 AND PLATE 19). Unfortunately, economics have prevented most of these ideas from ever reaching production.

The restoration and refurbishment of old lightplanes could allow the average aviation enthusiast to keep on flying. The cost of completely restoring an old airframe and engine to "like new" condition is substantially less than the purchase price of a brand-new airplane. In the case of the old airframe, liability-insurance and certification costs are almost nil. And if new avionics are added, plus perhaps an upgraded engine, the restored lightplane is just about as good as new, because lightplane performance has not changed dramatically. This means that the demand for used aircraft will be tremendous, and aircraft restoration businesses could be very profitable. Investments in used aircraft and refurbishments will be wise investments because lightplanes will be appreciating in value. As a result, many aircraft that might have been relegated to the scrapyard may be given a new lease on life.

HOMEBUILTS AND ULTRALIGHTS

While rapid incorporation of technological advances might not be the way of life in the lightplane industry, this is definitely not the case when it comes to the aircraft being assembled in garages, carports, and basements across America. Indeed, new ideas and completely new designs are the mainstay of these experimental-aircraft builders. Homebuilding is a thriving hobby, as witnessed by the tens of thousands of people that flock to the Experimental Aircraft Association's annual air show in Oshkosh, Wisconsin.

While many homebuilts look like future military and commercial aircraft, others resemble historic aircraft. These are the homebuilt, subscale versions of aircraft like the Spad or Fokker biplanes of World War I fame or the P-51 *Mustang* from World War II.

Burt Rutan has had a major impact on the homebuilt aircraft phenomenon. His designs, like the VariEze and Long-EZ, showed that canards could be successfully used on an aircraft the average pilot could safely fly (FIG. 9-12). He pioneered the use of fiberglass-on-foam construction and showed that it not only offered simple, low-cost construction, but it was also strong and its smooth surfaces resulted in reduced drag, the idea behind the natural laminar flow concept.

Even though he did not invent the idea of subscale flying prototypes, Burt Rutan made them a useful tool in aircraft development. Prototypes like the AD-1 oblique-wing demonstrator, the subscale

Fig. 9-6. An example of good concepts that do not change. In the upper photo is the Dornier *Wal* of the 1920s. The lower photo is the mostly composite Dornier *Seastar* currently under development. (Courtesy Clausius Dornier Seastar)

Fig. 9-7. The *Seawind,* a rather futuristic light seaplane from Canada. (Courtesy Seawind)

version of the Beechcraft *Starship I,* and the T-46A trainer allowed flight testing of new configurations at a fraction of the cost of a full-size flying prototype. By using composites, not only were the sub-scale prototypes built quickly and inexpensively,

changes in designs were easily incorporated and tested.

Because it takes so little time to incorporate new designs, compared to the long lead times in the military and commercial aviation business, it is difficult to project the types of homebuilts and ultralights that will be flying in the future. Ideas conceived today can be flying within a year, not by the year 2000. All that can really be said is that some of the ideas developed and proven in homebuilts can move upstream to more sophisticated aircraft. The *Starship I* is a perfect example of this. This aircraft's use of composites, canards, swept-back wings, winglets, and a rear-mounted pusher engine all reflect a definite Rutan-homebuilt influence.

Fig. 9-8. The *Sceptre* is one of the new generation of affordable recreational airplanes. Quite naturally, composites are used extensively. (Courtesy Marquardt & Roche)

Fig. 9-9. The *Monex,* a high-performing air recreational vehicle has set world speed records. (Courtesy Monnett Experimental Aircraft)

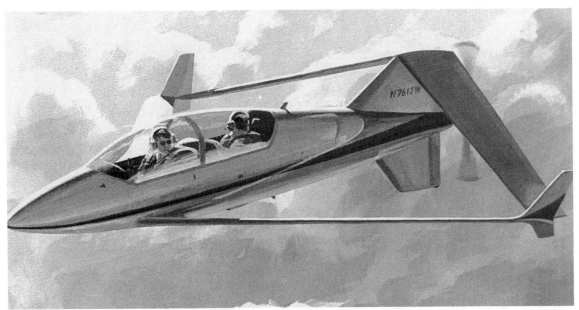

Fig. 9-10. A joined-wing recreational aircraft concept. (Copyright 1984 ACA Industries from a painting by Paul Fjeld)

Fig. 9-11. Even agricultural aircraft might take on new shapes, as suggested by this scale model that uses a joined wing. (Courtesy NASA)

Fig. 9-12. A couple of designs from the fertile mind of Burt Rutan. In the foreground is the Rutan *VariViggen*. The aircraft in the background is the *VariEze*. (Courtesy Rutan Aircraft Factory)

Fig. 9-13. A V/STOL commuter aircraft could operate from a landing pad in the inner city and still fly at reasonably high speeds. (Courtesy Bell Helicopters Textron)

V/STOL AIRCRAFT

While the primary impetus for the development of V/STOL transports will come from the military, concepts like the Bell *Osprey* tilt-rotor could find many civil applications (FIG. 9-13). Such an aircraft would be ideal in remote parts of the world where distances to be traveled are great and airfields are primitive or non-existent (one example that immediately comes to mind is island-hopping service in the Pacific). In addition, they would be a boon to the offshore petroleum industry, one of the major civilian users of helicopters. As near-shore petroleum deposits are depleted, exploration and production will have to be done at ranges beyond the capabilities of helicopters. Because V/STOLs are faster, less time would have to be spent in commuting to and from the rigs.

The tilt-rotor air-taxi or feeder airliner could operate from rather small landing areas and still offer the speed and range of a fixed-wing, turboprop aircraft. A cargo version would be perfect for air-express carriers to pick up cargo in small cities and rapidly transport it to large hub airports for transfer to the larger, long-distance air freighters. A tilt-rotor air ambulance could save precious minutes transporting critically-injured persons from the site of an emergency directly to the hospital.

Epilogue

IT IS OUR FERVENT HOPE THAT THE ADVANCES IN technology described here will be used to benefit mankind. While many of the advances are aimed at increasing military might, civilian and military leaders must be resolute in using this technology to insure peace and the preservation of freedoms. This requires the delicate balance symbolized in the Great Seal of the United States, where the eagle clutches the olive branch of peace in one claw and a brace of arrows in the other claw, representing the military ability to insure peace. This will not be an easy task, nor has it ever been.

Christ told his disciples,

> *"And you will be hearing of wars and rumors of wars; see that you are not frightened, for these things must take place, but that is not yet the end." (Matthew 24:6)*

Today's news is filled with wars and rumors of wars. And while the wars might not be on traditional battlefields, there is an ongoing struggle in the form of a high-technology arms race between the superpowers. Nowhere is this arms race more competitive than in the aerospace world.

Orville Wright best summed up our hope for aviation when, during the Great War, he said it was the brothers' hope that they were giving the world "an invention which would make further wars practically impossible." Unfortunately, history proved him wrong.

The Wright brothers discovered that flight, like peace, requires not only brute power, but also control and balance. With this wisdom of the first men to fly, may America put into operation the best aerospace vehicles in the 21st century.

173

Acknowledgments

ACA Industries, Inc.
    Dr. Julian Wolkovitch
    Paul Fjeld
Airbus Industrie of North America
Avco Lycoming
Avions Marcel Dassault-Breguet Aviation
    Henri Suisse
Avtek Corp.
    Robert D. Honeycutt
Beech Aircraft Corp.
    John Gedraitis
Bell Aerospace Textron
Bell Helicopters Textron
    Richard Tipton
Boeing Aerospace Co.
    William R. Jury
Boeing Commercial Airplane Co.
    John M. Swihart
Boeing Computer Services
    Maureen M. Herward
Boeing Military Airplane Co.
    Peter B. Dakan

Boeing Vertol Co.
British Aerospace
    Anne Case
Calspan Corporation
    Thomas J. Hanlon
Canadair
Claudius Dornier Seastar GmbH & Co. KG
Department of the Air Force
    Lt. Col. Joe Wagovitch
Department of the Air Force,
Aeronautical Systems Div.
    Lt. Tess Tate
    Jo Anne Rumple
    Helen A. Kavanaugh
Gates Learjet Corp.
General Dynamics
General Electric
    Ken Kilner
Goodyear Aerospace
    Bernard Scofield
    Lyle Schwilling
Grumman Aerospace Corp.

Gulfstream Aerospace Corp.
Honeywell, Inc.
Hughes Helicopters
INAV LTJ
    Carol Wolff
Lockheed California Co.
    Robert C. Ferguson
    Eric Schulzinger
    Syd Mead
Lockheed Georgia Co.,
Flight Sciences Division
    Steve Frank
    W.R. Paden Jr.
Lockheed Missile and Space Company
LTV Aerospace and Defense Co.
    Susan J. Laramee
Marquardt & Roche Co.
    Michael Figoff
McDonnell Douglas Astronautics Co.
    Robert L. Huss
McDonnell Douglas Corp.
    E.P. Bendel
    W.H. Brinks
    Bob Foster
    K. Moran
    D.N. Hanson
    Roger D. Schaufele
McDonnell Douglas Electronics Co.,
Polhemus Navigation Sciences Division
    David G. Bridges
Monnett Experimental Aircraft, Inc.
NASA Ames Research Center
    Jim Hawley
NASA Langley Research Center
    A. Gary Price
    Keith Henry
NASA Lewis Research Center
    Robert C. Hendricks
    Robert J. Simoneau
    John W. Dunning, Jr.
    Calvin L. Ball
NASA News
    Jim Hawley
Northrop Corp.
    Les Daly

Omac, Inc.
Phalanx Organizations
    William F. Moody
    Ron Sherman
Ramtek
    Regina Muccillo
Rockwell International, Inc.
    D.W. Sutherland
    D.L. Steelman
Rockwell International Satellite Systems Division
    K.A. Thomas
Rotex Engineering, Inc.
    James E. Sigsbee
Rutan Aircraft Factory, Inc.
    Burt Rutan
Sandia National Laboratory
Seawind
Singer Co., Link Flight Simulation Division
    Richard G. Adams
Stoddard Hamilton Aircraft, Inc.
Sundstrand Aviation Mechanical
    Robert A. Sweeney
Texas Instruments
    Wilma J. Smith
Titlis Fiber Composites LTD.
    Balz Knabenhans
TRW, Electronics and Technology Division
    Timothy L. Dolan
    Fred I. Alexander
United Technologies Pratt and Whitney
    Clip Glisson
United Technologies Sikorsky Aircraft
    James R. Bowman
    Fred C. Lash
Versatec Xerox Co.
    Pamela H. Simmons
Westinghouse Defense News
    D.H. Pierson
Westinghouse Electric Corp.
Westland Helicopters

Special thanks to Brian Siuru for proofreading and correcting the final manuscript.

Index

Other Bestsellers of Related Interest

REFLECTIONS OF A PILOT—Len Morgan

No Len Morgan fan will want to miss this one-time opportunity to have this collection of nearly five years of Len Morgan's most popular feature articles from *Flying* Magazine—55 in all! Here in a single, action-packed volume are all those Morgan columns you wish you had clipped and saved. Here, as only Morgan can tell them, are the stories and observations of what it was like to be a transport pilot in World War II, a co-pilot of an airline DC-3, and the captain of an intercontinental 747. 224 pages. Book No. 2398, $12.95 paperback only

VECTORS: The Author's Favorite Columns from Flying—Len Morgan

This third, and perhaps best, collection of witty and thought-provoking articles takes a warm and personal look at the people, places, and machines that have influenced Morgan during a career that spanned the days from propeller-driven airplanes to intercontinental jumbo jets. Each article presents a brief, but fascinating look into Morgan's personal experiences, and demonstrates why Morgan has become one of the most respected and widely read writers in aviation today. 240 pages, 60 illustrations. Book No. 3741, $14.95 paperback, $22.95 hardcover

THE FIRST TO FLY: Aviation's Pioneer Days
—Sherwood Harris

Based on diaries, letters, interviews, and newspaper reports, this book captures the color, adventure, resourcefulness, mechanical ingenuity, and perseverance of the men and women who turned their dreams of flying into reality. Whenever possible, the daring exploits of these fledgling aviators are told in their own words and the words of those who witnessed the great events that marked the early days of aviation, from 1900 to 1915. 240 pages, 72 illustrations. Book No. 3796, $14.95 paperback, $24.95 hardcover

THE ILLUSTRATED GUIDE TO AERODYNAMICS—2nd Edition
—H. C. "Skip" Smith

Avoiding technical jargon and scientific explanations, this guide demonstrates how aerodynamic principles affect every aircraft in terms of lift, thrust, drag, in-air performance, stability, and control. It includes new material on airfoil development and design, accelerated climb performance, takeoff velocities, load and velocity-load factors, hypersonic flight, area rules, laminar flow airfoils, planform shapes, computer-aided design, and high-performance lightplanes. 352 pages, 269 illustrations. Book No. 3786, $18.95 paperback only

THE LADY BE GOOD: Mystery Bomber of World War II—Dennis E. McClendon

What happened to the B-24 bomber nicknamed "The Lady Be Good," and its nine young American crewmembers when they vanished without a trace in 1943? Sixteen years later the perfectly preserved B-24 was found deep in the Sahara desert—440 miles from its base? Why was it there and where was its crew? An official search resulted in this incredible tale that pieces together the solution to the bomber's mysterious fate. 208 pages. Illustrated. Book No. 26624, $12.95 paperback only

GENERAL AVIATION LAW—Jerry A. Eichenberger

Although the regulatory burden that is part of flying sometimes seems overwhelming, it need not take the pleasure out of your flight time. This survey of aviation regulations gives you a solid understanding of FAA procedures and functions, airman ratings and maintenance certificates, the implications of aircraft ownership, and more. It allows you to recognize legal problems before they result in FAA investigations and potentially serious consequences. 240 pages. Book No. 3431, $16.95 paperback, $25.95 hardcover

LEARJETS: The World's Executive Aircraft
—Donald J. Porter

Here's the riveting inside story of the evolution, development, production, and flight performance of the Learjet series, including absorbing accounts of how the modern executive jet evolved. You'll find breathtaking photographs and illustrations that depict the aircraft's innovative design, detailed specifications, and performance data for every model built. 128 pages, 32 illustrations. Book No. 2440, $11.95 paperback only

STEALTH STRIKE—Frank J. O'Brien

Set in 1995, this is a suspense-packed novel of human valor and high-tech military prowess. Star Wars satellites are up and the Russians want them down. The action builds and America's daring preemptive strike puts you inside the cockpit where you'll experience the longest, most grueling edge-of-the-seat dogfight you're ever likely to encounter. 264 pages. Book No. 3472, $16.95 hardcover only

Prices Subject to Change Without Notice.

Look for These and Other TAB Books at Your Local Bookstore

To Order Call Toll Free 1-800-822-8158
(24-hour telephone service available.)

or write to TAB Books, Blue Ridge Summit, PA 17294-0840.

Title	Product No.	Quantity	Price

☐ Check or money order made payable to TAB Books

Charge my ☐ VISA ☐ MasterCard ☐ American Express

Acct. No. _____ Exp. _____

Signature: _____

Name: _____

Address: _____

City: _____

State: _____ Zip: _____

Subtotal $ _____

Postage and Handling
($3.00 in U.S., $5.00 outside U.S.) $ _____

Add applicable state and local
sales tax $ _____

TOTAL $ _____

TAB Books catalog free with purchase; otherwise send $1.00 in check or money order and receive $1.00 credit on your next purchase.

Orders outside U.S. must pay with international money order in U.S. dollars drawn on a U.S. bank.

TAB Guarantee: If for any reason you are not satisfied with the book(s) you order, simply return it (them) within 15 days and receive a full refund. **BC**